"Our heart wants only the best for us. Ayelet's third book in the *F*ck The Bucket List* Trilogy compels us to go within to uncover the deepest desires within our hearts. Trekking into the unknown is about trusting our inner voice, the calling within our heart.

No one else knows what is best for us. Only we know what is best for us. We are the creators of our destiny. We must let the magic of our hearts guide us to create happiness, joy, and freedom consciously."

– Carol Chapman, *Host of Hearts Rise Up Podcast and Community, Heart-centered Guide, Author, Speaker*

"Sometimes you come across a trilogy of books that speak to you deeply and personally. Except to nod your head in agreement, feel the challenge of going against the grain and the exciting pull of personal adventure. Ayelet Baron will take you on a trek into the unknown, one from which you will never want to come back."

– Kay Newton, Author and Midlife Strategist

"The timing of this book couldn't be more perfect. As our world continues to change, so many people, myself included, have been forced to look deeply at the ways we work and live, at how we relate and connect with one another, and how we choose to take care of ourselves. Already so many norms have been blown apart, giving us a huge opportunity to change our course. What do we keep? What do we leave behind?

As the leader of a community of female founders where we regularly connect, collaborate and co-create, this book is particularly valuable for me, as I suspect it may be for others. It is a guide to not only how to ensure you care for yourself, but also in exploring new ways of caring for each other as we build new paths together.

*F*ck the Bucket List for the Health Conscious* is an excellent guide to the questions we will have as leaders of the new world. It opens up possibilities for us all as to what's next. Don't miss the opportunity to have Ayelet as your guide."

– Jenn LeBlanc, author, *Changing Tides: Powerful Strategies for Female Founders* and *Launching for Revenue*. Founder, Changing Tides Movement and ThinkResults

"Ayelet Baron's trilogy of *F*ck the Bucket List* is truly an empowering read. Ayelet poses questions that are critically important for this time in our evolution and more importantly-for our survival.

Many of us have been so conditioned to giving our power away by yielding it to the status quo that we have lost our individual voices and as a result, compromised our collective future. Ayelet reminds us that we each have a voice and provides the space to explore what that is and to unapologetically use it. A must read!"

— Tammy McCrary
Artist Advocate, Author, and Founder of Artistology

"*F*ck the Bucket List for the Health Conscious :Trusting Your Heart* helps us examine the unhealthy role fear plays in our world by exposing stories of influencers and experts we have been conditioned to trust. It helps us discover, at our own pace, what and who is for us, and who isn't, by listening deeply and questioning everything. We learn that we don't need to stay in a divided world of winners and losers. We begin to see the abundant opportunities that lie in front of us. This may be the last book in the trilogy, but just the beginning of creating what's possible in our lives and our communities."

— Tim McDonald, Former Director of
Community, The Huffington Post

"*F*ck the Bucket List* trilogy is a primer for the courageous heart on the journey to true self-discovery. Ayelet does not do the work for you in this process of divine discovery but she points the way across the threshold. As she says, the way forward involves action and commitment to a goal which might seem hazy, but she is there as a companion to accompany you on perhaps the greatest adventure of your lifetime. The journey to YOU!"

— Flicka Rahn, musician, author, sound healer and educator

"*F*ck the Bucket List for the Health Conscious* is an extraordinary 'radically change your life' curriculum to listen to the 'whispers of your heart' and finally be bold enough to live YOUR unique and beautiful life. Grab a pencil and paper because you'll get busy doing imaginative and inspirational practices in the first few pages of this fabulously written book!

Ayelet, with the Universe, gives us a 'Divinely Disruptive' story about what's not working in our human design. She exposes the fears that drive our decisions in health, relationships, love, money, and what we've constructed in this 'Houston we've got a problem' reality. And then she offers up the 'Medicine' from both her very personal life experiences and many beautiful people who have undergone their own transformation to provide potent truths that instantly enhance your life.

Ayelet's years of being a sought after corporate wiz to a futurist with wisdom borne from loss, faith, trauma, truth and most importantly self-love and service to help others thrive is a gifted guide. In each Chapter/ Expedition, you'll find ways to ignite the True You. And through your imagination, boldness and courage, you'll take the steps right here right now to manifest your Soul's purpose. And how to reconnect to your best friend ever—Nature! A key ingredient for living in deep love and unity with Grand Earth and each other.

Take your time on this best ever summer read! I felt myself getting so excited to get to the next Expedition because something magical happened to me on my own journey to live a wildly spontaneous and joyful life! The *F*ck the Bucket* list trilogy inspired me on such a deep personal level that I now have a grazing plan to restore Bison habitat near the New Mexico border to heal the soil and Soul of GrandMother Earth on the land I call Oniya, which means 'to breathe.' This book guided me to go deep inside myself and continue charting the course for a healthy life filled with possibilities."

– Tara Sheahan, Founder, Conscious Global Leadership LLC
Oniya 'Restoring Bison and Biodiversity to heal GrandMother Earth', and
Breathelab 'Natural nose breathing to rewire for happiness'

F♥CK THE BUCKET LIST

FOR THE HEALTH CONSCIOUS

Trusting Your Heart

Book 3

THE UNIVERSE WITH
AYELET BARON

Visit ayeletbaron.com for more information
Published by HeartPickings.com
Editing, design, and distribution by Bublish Inc.

Hardback ISBN: 978-1-647043-36-0
Paperback ISBN: 978-1-647043-35-3
eBook ISBN: 978-1-647043-34-6

DEDICATION

This book is for you if…

You are in love with the mystery of life.

You dream of being free to be who you truly are.

You are here to live a healthy and meaningful
life as a powerful creator who cares deeply about
yourself, your community, and the planet.

You question everything and say fuck it—or whatever words
you choose to use—when something in life no longer serves
you. You know this by listening to the whispers of your heart.

WELCOME BACK FOR THE THIRD LEG OF OUR JOURNEY!

Remember the many compartments of the heart, the seed of what is possible. So much of who we are is defined by the places we hold for each other.

For it is not our ingenuity that sets us apart, but our capacity for love, the possibility our way will be lit by grace.

Our hearts prisms, chiseling out the colors of pure light.

Kare Anderson

Emmy-winning journalist, author, and TED speaker

OUR ITINERARY
TABLE OF CONTENTS

♥

LISTENING TO THE WHISPERS OF YOUR HEART

INTRODUCTION

♥

When we set out on a journey, we usually know where we're going—often we think we do, when we don't really have a clue. In November 2016, I took a leap of faith and left San Francisco to start a new adventure. I moved to a remote town with people I thought I trusted. I had never heard of Lund or the Sunshine Coast of British Columbia before, but during my first visit, I fell in love with its natural beauty, expansiveness, and tranquility. Living close to the ocean had always been a dream of mine but living in a rural community was entirely unknown to me. I had spent much of my life in large urban concrete jungles (cities) and was accustomed to having easy access to anything I desired, be it work, entertainment, art, healthy food, or friends. But I left it all behind to trek into the unknown—to explore possibilities.

The intention of creating something purposeful was exciting, and my enthusiasm and trust blinded me from truly seeing that the people I had bet on were not healthy for my well-being. They talked a good game, and I allowed myself to be hooked into their vision, but when it came to actions and creating what was most needed in unity, there were always excuses and reasons why we couldn't do it. The talk was louder than the ability to execute something meaningful, together, in community. And it wasn't anyone's fault that it all fell apart. But the real reason I came to this town was not to build something with them but to have a place deep in the rainforest to connect with nature, become health conscious, and let these three books flow out into the world.

Sometimes our biggest gifts are disguised as what society calls failures and disappointments. Healing is an inside job. Challenges become problems when we allow ourselves to react without taking the time to think and feel through situations. Sometimes our heart is calling us to weed out what is obstructing the energy at our core, and many of us have learned not to listen to its call. But strength comes from facing our challenges and moving away from the norm by transforming them into our greatest opportunities. When we can look at a challenge and examine its root cause, we take a step toward self-awareness and mastery. We are always free to choose our own experience and adventure, even at times when the external world is calling us to take sides and fight for our lives—which is the current story of our times.

I had two choices: stay in an unhealthy partnership or listen deeply to the warnings my heart was whispering. I did not know at the outset of this expedition that I had come to this peaceful little town to get in touch with my own roots, learn from nature, and heal. And in 2020, when the global pandemic was unleashed, I felt gratitude to the universe for providing me with these choices, because if I had been successful with these partners, I would have ended up with a conscious leadership academy at the edge of the world that no one could travel to because of the lockdowns. And once again, I tapped into the universal wisdom that there are no accidents. Maybe the Universe conspired to help me practice my ability to adapt to change?

Nature teaches us that deviating from the norm and staying in flow is how we thrive. And it need not be a battle of survival. The natural world thrives when it adapts to change by becoming stronger and more resilient. While the hungry bear may have climbed the plum tree in our yard and snapped a branch with its weight, a new branch is waiting to emerge and flourish with new fruit. A healthy tree will always find a way to birth new fruit despite the hardships it faces. Each of us has been gifted and wired with this same potential, and our heart is simply waiting for us to tap into our true abilities and flow with our natural rhythms.

Living in the midst of nature entirely changed my life and provided an opportunity for me to learn from her pure fierceness and beauty. I learned to connect with the heartbeat of the earth and listen to the deep whispers of my heart. I was reminded that we are not separate from nature and that there's a natural flow to everything. But by no means has it been easy. Like any of us, my inner self was waiting patiently for me to begin a healthier chapter in life and unlearn much that had been stuffed inside me by those who had walked their own paths before me and felt they knew what was best for me. I learned to ask questions and get to the source of everything, because no one had *my* answers, especially people who didn't bother to find out what my questions were because they had a predetermined agenda of their own.

Sometimes our destination is not clear, and it's hard to face the unknown because we've been led to believe that we should always have clear goals in order to achieve success in life. Why else do so many of us greet every New Year with resolutions? Why would depression, burnout, loneliness, and stress-induced diseases be spiraling so high among so many of us? Why have we been brought up to believe that we're here to achieve more and more success? Why have we been taught that happiness itself is a destination, and we're seen as "losers" when we fail to attain it?

When we travel along our path, we can become increasingly aware that there is no destination in life—just life itself. Many well-known authors have written about being present and appreciating the moment—a task that has proven to be challenging for many of us, as it's out of alignment with societal pressures to achieve and become a "someone" who is celebrated and known.

ONE DAY YOU BREAK FREE

You may not know where you're headed on your path, but at a certain point you become more courageous and curious to experience life and all it has to offer. And this is where you may find yourself right now. The rest of your journey is in front of you, mysterious and unknown. The darkest hours can be behind you when you do your work and choose to trek into the unknown. And to do so, you jump into the third leg of our journey where you wholeheartedly begin to trust your heart, your intuition, and the deep whispers of the universe. When you start listening and becoming fully aware of what's healthy and what's toxic for you—when it comes to the people you put in your heart, the beliefs you put in your mind, and the food and products your body consumes—you become a healthy, conscious creator of your life.

As more of us awaken to the voice deep within us, we will understand that when we come together in unity, not conformity or uniformity, our collective journey on this planet will also transform.

There are stories in this book of courageous people who are transforming education, fashion, health, and agriculture, for example; they are included simply to make you curious enough to connect with them and with others who are creating healthy systems. Instead of trying to save or fix our broken systems, there is an opportunity to create what is needed most.

Each of us is here to do our work in addressing our wounds and traumas in our own way; we dove into this in the first two books of this trilogy. You are the only one who can lead yourself out of your own darkness to live a healthy life. What if you could have more joy, less stress, and more energy to play? What would it be like to no longer frantically obsess over "achieving" or winning the good life?

We are all fumbling along, doing the best we can with what we know and have. As we explored in the first two books of this trilogy, it's up to each of us to direct our attention and energy toward what and who is healthy and away from what and who is toxic for our mental, emotional, and physical health. Intentions are key as we take our first steps in being consciously aware of whether people have healthy intentions beneath their words and actions. And we are always seeking to understand the root cause of our own intentions and actions. We have an opportunity to become increasingly aware of whether we are acting out of fear, guilt, shame, or a sense of having to be responsible. This is where living in alignment and tapping into our heart guides and directs us into healthy actions and outcomes and away from stressful situations and people.

Had I not moved to Lund, I would never have met my friends Janet and Rob Southcott, who are part of a local community creating Blueberry Commons, a cohousing and food security cooperative in Powell River. They are beautiful, heart-filled people who have brought joy into my life. Rob was a paramedic for many years and is now on the local city council, and Janet is a talented artist and writer. It was serendipity that we met, since I have mostly kept to myself and have not integrated into the local community, except for most of my wonderful neighbors.

Over long dinner conversations, we explore the edges. We talk about how our current reality is based on values and assumptions that we are separate individuals competing for our very survival and success. In this story, we are victims of the world where there are heroes who will save us from it all, if we choose to put our trust and faith in them. But what if we choose to take a different path and deeply question this construct that no longer makes sense to many of us? What if we looked inside ourselves and saw the beliefs, values, and assumptions buried there and questioned whether they were really ours? What if we no longer believed that we are victims of a system that is making us sick and truly understood our capacity to cocreate what is needed most right now? What if we became aware that we don't have to be victims of a dying system but can create what we need?

The old structures are falling apart, and it's a divine opportunity to become aware that anything that separates and divides you from yourself and others is unhealthy. When you remember you are part of nature and start listening to your heart's internal guidance and igniting your imagination, then what emerges will be healthy thinking, a healthy ego, and healthy living. Do you realize that you didn't come to this planet only to suffer, survive, achieve, and fight for your life? This is an old soundtrack that no longer serves many of us, and isn't this a great opportunity to listen to something that resonates with who you truly are?

No one is coming to save you. No one has your answers. And think about it: if they did, would our world look the way it does today? There is a false belief on the planet that our political, financial, legal, health, education, and many other systems are the ones you must adhere to. But in reality, most of those no longer serve the vast majority of us. And until you go on your own journey and unlearn and uncondition from what no longer serves you, you stay trapped in a divided world, rather than choosing to spend your life writing healthy stories for yourself.

Leadership is not outside yourself, and it's your time to understand that you don't need false prophets, leaders, or profits to have a full life. It's time for health-conscious souls to take our place in history and step into our power. Were you not born for these times? Can you see yourself stepping out of the manual of how you were taught life should be, to trek into the unknown and follow your heart's calling?

This isn't just another self-help book, spiritual book, or memoir— it's an experience, beyond categories and labels, that asks each of us to tap into the universal wisdom that says we can live our lives our own way. I'd like to share up front that this book is not for everyone. It's for those of us ready to start questioning everything and to simply say "fuck it"—or whatever words you choose to use—when something in life no longer serves you. The *F*ck the Bucket List* book trilogy has been created not to dictate meaning, but to inspire you to ask questions, dig deep, and create your *own* meaning.

Each one of your stories starts and ends at your pace. Once you connect with your own rhythm, you can go on an adventure of a lifetime. These books, like a journey, are a collaboration with the expansiveness of the universe. I hope you take many things out of them that help you lead a healthy life by questioning everything. It's up to you to realize whom you trust and where your power lies. As for me, I can no longer afford to put my trust in the hands of politicians, philanthropists, business leaders, or any one person. A hero-or-victim society is simply not for me. I want to cocreate and weave with deep compassion, knowing that there is another way to live a healthy life than what I was sold and taught.

CAN YOU DANCE WITH POSSIBILITIES?

Life is shaped from the inside out, and much is possible when we dance with the possibilities it abundantly offers us. For some reason, we're taught not to hurt others but that it's okay to imprison ourselves in a world of never-ending fear and conflict. "Courage," Plato wrote, "is knowing what is not to be feared." And that's what I love about truly being human: feeling into everything—from joy to grief—and becoming consciously aware of who and what we're consuming and creating with. As we amass life experiences, with the richness of our own adventures in failure and success, we learn not to sweat the small stuff by squandering our energy on things that don't matter or that are toxic to our well-being.

My hope is that you discover what matters most to you, when no one is looking or judging, and listen to the deep whispers of your heart while standing grounded in Mother Earth. Living each day from your heart, regardless of how young or old you are, is the boldest and most authentic journey you'll take. The philosopher Confucius, in *The Analects*, depicts the cycle of life as a journey that takes you closer to your own heart and the Divine. "At 15 I set my heart on learning. At 30 I took my stand. At 40 I came to be free from doubts. At 50 I understood the decree of heaven. At 60 my ear was attuned. At 70 I followed my heart's desire without overstepping the line." Can you change your story and follow your heart, at any age, and dance in possibilities?

It's up to you whether you layer more items on your bucket list or simply slow down, pause, feel deeply into your being, root in the ground, connect with yourself, build your community, and share your natural beauty with the world. There's no real need to struggle during your journey when you realize there's no destination and that "getting there" is playing a part in someone else's story. What if, by tapping into your heart, you're already here, and you allow yourself to play and experiment as a health-conscious creator? What then? What's whispering to you? Are you ready to listen?

Enjoy your journey!

With eternal gratitude,
The Universe with Ayelet

EXPEDITION 19

ARE YOU KEEPING ROOM IN YOUR HEART FOR THE UNIMAGINABLE?

♥

A musician shared many of his life stories with me, and now I want to share one of my favorites with you. In the 1970s, his band was invited to perform all over South Africa. He was sitting on a lawn chair by the hotel's pool when a local drummer asked him why he was not out exploring the countryside.

He was enjoying the sun's rays after playing long into the night. He asked the drummer, "Where do you think I can go that's better than this heavenly spot?"

The drummer laughed heartily and said, "You are in the heart of Durban and there's an adventure waiting for you at the Valley of a Thousand Hills if you can pry yourself from that chair." The drummer handed him a joint and said, "Here's some Durban Poison for when you get there, but you need to go easy on it."

The musician jumped into the blue convertible he'd rented. As he drove toward the valley, he found himself climbing higher and higher on a road with almost no traffic. When he got to the valley, he saw that the hills were covered with vibrant purple flowers. He parked the car on a dirt road. He then lit the joint and took in the beauty of the mighty Umgeni River, which flowed from the distant Drakensberg Mountains to the warm, inviting Indian Ocean.

After a few minutes, the effects of the plant he'd smoked hit him, and he was not sure if what he was seeing was real or not. He thought he saw a native Zulu man walking toward him. His face was painted with different colors and he was wearing feathers. It looked like his eyes were popping out of their sockets, and the musician wondered if this man had been smoking Durban Poison since he woke up that morning. But the man looked very kind.

The musician said hello and soon realized the man knew only a few words of English.

The man pointed to himself and said "Thabo" and reached for the musician's hand, signaling that he should come with him.

The musician tried to tell him with hand gestures that he needed to go back to his car. But Thabo was insistent, and so the musician found himself following this man dressed in feathers, down the hill.

When they had walked a short way down the path, a Zulu village emerged below. The musician saw bare-chested women running around, children playing on the ground, and chickens and pigs freely exploring the village. It was a scene of joy. The Durban Poison was making its way through his system and he felt as if he was experiencing a magical moment in time.

The musician felt far away from the rigid laws of segregation that he had experienced during his South Africa tour. Just a few days earlier, he had almost been arrested by a police officer who'd stopped his car as he was giving a local musician a ride home in the rain. The apartheid law stated that you were not allowed to be alone in a car with a black man. There had to be at least two white people in the vehicle. It was pouring rain but the policeman hadn't cared, and no amount of reasoning helped.

And now, the musician felt as if he had walked into another time and space. No one knew he was coming, but it was as though this was where he was supposed to be. When they reached the village, Thabo showed him where to sit. Food started to appear in front of him, served in ancient-looking, wooden containers. For the Zulu people, eating from the same plate was, and still is, a sign of friendship. He took in all the delicious flavors, sounds, and scenes that enveloped him in a place filled with life. He enjoyed listening to their music and experiencing how they flowed so effortlessly. He was having the time of his life.

They used their hands to communicate and somehow understood each other. It wasn't like they were talking about politics or deep issues. They were simply connecting, and their conversation consisted mostly of saying yes or no or thank you with their eyes. He felt that he had a rare glimpse of being in a caring community of people who accepted each other with no strings attached. They had very few material things and yet they emanated joy in the midst of the hell the country was going through.

This is what can happen when you throw out the manual of how life should be lived and trek into the unknown with an open heart. There's a deep knowing we can each trust—our internal compass—that is always in tune with the notion that everything is already here to be discovered. The love of a healthy heart and the expansiveness of a healthy mind come together with a synergy that can change your life.

When the musician thinks back to some of the situations he got himself into, it sometimes scares him in retrospect. He wonders whether he was courageous or simply crazy to jump into new adventures. But he rarely feels afraid while he is in one of these adventures because he has learned to follow his heart and his intuition. Instead of feeding into any fear or tension, he simply trusts his curiosity and imagination. Because it is usually the truth.

BECOMING AWARE OF FLOW

Every thought that you bring with you in every moment of the day is continually transforming you. Your mind is a strong vessel that you allow to govern you. You can start your day mired in fears, limitations, and sadness and have them drag you down. A situation may be playing in your head over and over, and that feeling of disappointment with how you mishandled it can easily become your theme song. Many of us have been conditioned to believe and trust others more than ourselves—it's the notion that there's some authority figure or expert who knows what's best for us.

Whatever beliefs you hold create the destination of thought and your day-to-day reality, and yet there is also a physical reality you need to be increasingly aware of. It's not like you can snap your fingers and transform your physical reality with a thought. A Tesla or a soulmate won't magically appear at your front door. It requires conscious effort, choice, intention, and the flow of pure energy. You stand at a crossroads of possibilities. You can choose to allow in a healthy thought or an unhealthy thought, each directing your life. That's how powerful you are. When you're aware of your power and energy source, you can open your heart to fresh opportunities. Every action you take and every thought that comes before it connects you to possibilities and outcomes that were not available before.

Knowing your own heart can shift your life in both revolutionary and small ways. But it requires alignment between what your mind tells you and what your heart and your intuition are whispering deep inside of you. Before acting on the thoughts that come to you, which you've been conditioned to listen to from your mind, you can go deep into your heart and listen like never before. And no one can tell you what's going on deep inside of you. You can become aware that belief lives in the mind and hope is carried in the heart. Imagine what can transpire when they're aligned and playing in harmony, just like a symphony.

To create, you align your actions with your words. You can say you are healthy and yet continue to consume sugary soda pop and deep-fried food, which are most likely unhealthy for your body. You can say you care about the environment and yet choose to consume products from companies that pollute the environment, are cruel to animals, or treat people poorly. What actions are you taking—are they unconscious or fully conscious? By examining your thoughts and checking whether they're aligned (healthy) or misaligned (toxic), you become increasingly conscious of your choices and their impact on your life. As we will explore in the next Expedition, you have within you so much that can be released.

Rumi, the thirteenth-century Persian poet, reminds us that "everyone has been made for some particular work, and the desire for that work has been put in our heart." You choose whether you're facing opportunities or challenges. You can create peace within yourself or you can war with yourself and those around you. When you imagine from the heart, you become aware that everything begins with a single thought in your mind. You have the ability, on your own or in a community, to imagine and create.

You are in charge of how you respond and react. When you came into this world, you were wired and given gifts. But over time, your conditioning and education may have taken you away from leading with your heart's capacity for compassion, abundance, and connection and was dominated by being rooted in material existence, goals, and achievements. At this stage of the journey, tapping into compassion for all things becomes foundational.

As a child, you experienced life and did not judge because you had not been *taught* how to judge yet. Imagine if you looked at our society now and saw people simply allowing self-compassion to navigate us to joy. Instead, today you will mostly see people judging and blaming ourselves and each other, while endlessly pursuing a state of fabricated happiness and success.

Getting to the root cause of our judgments is one way of healing, but it is somewhat difficult for many of us who have been conditioned to believe that our thoughts need to be right and are more important than anyone else's. And you may be caught up in a constant need to validate your position, because allowing any other thinking challenges you to the core. In my case, I started to become more of an observer of what was happening around me and experienced the divisions, especially when someone wanted to prove me wrong. At some point in our interaction, I would stop and agree with them. And what I experienced was their disbelief and need to continue to be right. But when I would say, "You're right" and pause for a moment and then say, "Now what?" they had nothing to say. They lived for the thrill of the fight. I don't want to fight anymore. I envision healthy, new possibilities for communication opening up between people when we no longer feel a need to win and crush someone else.

I wanted to be healthy and clean out the toxicity of judging, blaming, and shaming around me. But it wasn't just about the external world; I also looked at where I was judging *myself* harshly and keeping myself divided with beliefs that were planted deep inside of me as a child when I was taught to be a *good* girl. I would find myself being incredibly self-critical, which always brought with it a sense of deep shame at being instructed that I was doing something wrong. Until I understood where this shame lived inside of me, it held me captive in old, painful stories. I asked myself the same question when I was deep in self-judgment: Now what?

I learned that I could take little baby steps, putting one foot in front of the other as I made my way into the unknown territory outside the confines of the old programming. So, when you find yourself struggling in your life, can you bring self-compassion and compassion for others into the picture? The conscious energy you bring into flow helps you close doors that lead nowhere, so that healthy windows and paths can emerge.

ARE YOU A MASTER SANDWICH MAKER?

A child or parent who does not know where their next meal will come from has a dream to never worry about being hungry. They have no idea what it is like to have a well-stocked refrigerator or to have food sit around for so long that it goes bad and has to be thrown out. Life is guided meal by meal. The only focus is where to find shelter, food, and clean water to make it through another day. The dream is to never go to sleep hungry. Once they are no longer hungry, a new dream emerges.

When you face which energy and resources are truly scarce and which are abundant in your life, you become aware of what you have access to. There's also an opportunity to understand what and who is for you and what and who is not for you. The question is, how much do you want it and how much energy will you invest in yourself? Your ability to dream and believe you can do it matters. Your capacity to create is sparked when you truly trust that you are on your path. Are you in touch with a tantalizing source of energy that teases you to explore life's next adventure? "The only true voyage of discovery, the only fountain of Eternal Youth, would be not to visit strange lands but to possess other eyes, to behold the universe through the eyes of another, of a hundred others, to behold the hundred universes that each of them beholds, that each of them is; and ... with men like these, we do really fly from star to star, "shares novelist Marcel Proust.

Someone can be a fountain of knowledge and yet lack imagination. Many of us have great ideas and dreams, and it's not always easy to know how to make them real. You may put them on a list, hoping to achieve them someday, or hoping your children or someone else might achieve them for you when they are older. But what if you could learn how to live your intentions on a daily basis, one step at a time?

All it takes is some action, the courage to take a few steps to start creating, and at the same time learning when to flow and when to slow down. Do you see a wave of opportunity in front of you or a pile of problems? So much depends on your mindset and how you choose to see situations. Did you grow up believing it was your job to help others fulfill their dreams and that theirs were more important than yours? Who put these thoughts in your mind? Can you trace them back to their source and focus your thinking now on trusting yourself and your intuition to fully live your life? Maybe instead of going through all the reasons why it's impossible, you can wrestle with all the reasons why you can begin.

I was asked a simple question a few years ago about whether I ever made eggs for breakfast or dinner. And now I have a question for you: Have you ever made a sandwich, and if so, did you know why you chose to make a sandwich when there were other meals you could have made? There are a variety of ways to make a sandwich, and one of the decisions in the process is to decide what type of bread to use—sourdough, rye, multigrain, whole wheat, or white bread. And in today's abundant world—for those who have access to food—you can even choose bread that is gluten-free! Or a roll, a bagel, a baguette, a croissant, a tortilla, a wrap, pita bread, or lettuce.

Let's say you choose sourdough bread. The next step will be deciding whether to toast the bread or eat it fresh. Will you spread butter, mustard, ghee, mayo, or hot sauce? Will you grill it and make a panini? And what will you put in it? Are you making it for yourself or will you be sharing with other people?

There are many decisions you need to make during this simple process. Will you make an open-faced sandwich? What level of heat will you use if you toast the bread? How will you serve it? Will you slice tomatoes and garnish the dish? Will you include condiments like pickles or kimchi? Even in the simplest of activities, you have a vision of what you want to create and you take action to execute it. Too often, you probably don't realize how much you already know and may find yourself unsure of your ability to make things happen. And an important question you may forget to ask is this: In an abundant world of food choices for those with means, why are you making a sandwich? Was it because you had all the ingredients and it was your only option, or were you craving it?

When you become aware of how you execute simple tasks like making a sandwich and what choices you make in the process, you can start to see how qualified you are to make *anything* happen in your life. Everything you do is based on the choices and decisions you make. When you become conscious and aware, you will see the wave of opportunities always within your reach. Sometimes you can do it yourself, and other times you can invite others who share your desire to collaborate and actualize what you imagine.

Here are some questions to ask yourself; please add your own or change them to make them work for you. It can be as small as working on a part of yourself or as big as you envision, like crossing the Atlantic Ocean in a paddleboat. Ask yourself: Do I have a dream? Is it really mine? What is my dream? How do I visualize and imagine it? What is my biggest opportunity? What's motivating and driving me? Are there any limiting beliefs or constraints that I need to address? Can I do it on my own, or do I need help? Are there people who share my dream? Do I know them? Can I connect with them? How do I find them? Is this a collective dream? Who can I dream with? How will I bring it to life? What is my "enough" when it comes to this dream? Of course, you will want to customize your own questions as you set out on your exploration.

Remember, this is an opportunity to live your signature life. You can experiment and add ingredients, side dishes, and garnishes as you see fit. Like a sandwich, you can make your own version with any combination of elements that appeals to your unique taste. Great dishes are made from fresh ingredients and come from the heart and soul of the chef who loves to cook and share their creations.

If you don't enjoy cooking, another way to think about this is in relation to how you take care of your body. When you decide to go in the direction of taking impeccable care of your body, you can start slowly by doing some stretching and yoga every few days to build a little bit of stamina. Then you may start to walk for twenty minutes every day. Gradually, you may add time and distance to your walks. Before long, you start to enjoy this practice and look forward to your daily walk and yoga. One day you wake up and realize how much healthier you feel and how much more energy you have for life. You will be very surprised with yourself—how capable you are and how strong and vigorous your body feels because of your commitment to increase your strength and take care of your whole body.

Whether it's experimenting with sandwiches, getting a book published, or healing your body, the path is the same as the path to actualizing your dreams. You can't go from imagination to reality without understanding the effort required. But you can birth a pure intention and begin. Finding meaning in why you are doing it is foundational. Understand the intention behind what you want to do and why you want to do it. Getting clarity does not need to be cumbersome. Ask yourself a lot of questions and gain clarity for yourself. Be conscious and real about what it will take to create and whether the path is a healthy one or one that will drain your energy. It takes a lot of energy to invest in an idea from your imagination and make it a reality. As an example, you can't imagine the coordination necessary and the amount of frustration, heartbreak, goodwill, energy, and resources that have been expended to see the final outcome of these books doing their work in our world.

A plan of action is only as good as your understanding of yourself—your abilities and limitations. Knowing yourself will keep you grounded and able to really assess any situation. Can you also take a close look at your fears and whether they are rational (like not walking into oncoming traffic) or irrational (like believing you are not good enough)? Knowing your fears will break down barriers before they appear or will allow you to navigate around them. Much is possible when you become aware of how much you want to create and whether you are driven by pure intentions. It is easy to play around with ideas in your head and never do anything with them. It can be euphoric to get lost in imagination, but what is your heart aching for? If you find yourself not taking action, perhaps this is not coming from your soul's purpose.

When an intention or dream doesn't let you go and keeps reappearing, listen carefully, because it is your intuition speaking to you from a deep place. If you are serious about actualizing your intentions, here are some thoughts:

- ♥ Ask yourself: What do I imagine?
- ♥ Imagine what it looks like to have it. Add qualities and characteristics to the imagining that make it real.

- ♥ Find the feeling of having it and feel that, right now, until the feeling has entered your heart and bones.

- ♥ Now, give it up, and let the universe sort out the details. Don't get too attached, as there may be lessons still to be learned regardless of how ready you feel.

- ♥ Take small steps to make it real, fail often along the way, and become aware and conscious of your choices. Listen to your heart and body and stay aligned with nature and what's natural for your well-being.

Many people run marathons. It takes dedication to run a marathon—great mental toughness and physical stamina to keep up the momentum to practice. You might be like my friend Claire, who started with a quarter marathon and worked her way up to a full marathon. Then she ran another one, and then others, until it became a way of life. Some women, after the birth of their first child, say they will never go through childbirth again. But after a while they are pregnant again, excited about having a newborn. Some folks ride a roller coaster over and over again, even though they scream and yell when they get to the top and maybe even throw up. And yet they go back. The jubilation and exhilaration of the ride bring the biggest satisfaction there is in the world—to pursue something that challenges us to go back.

Until you truly value and love yourself to the core, the rest is simply noise. It is easy to fall into the trap of trying to please all the people all the time and end up losing sight of yourself. You can ask: Is my life my own, or have I allowed other people, fate, or circumstances to dictate my path? To whom have I given authority over my existence? Who truly supports me unconditionally? How am I making room in my heart for the unimaginable?

EXPEDITION 20

EXPERIMENTING WITH EVERYTHING

We live on a fine line between the very sad and the extremely humorous aspects of life. In many respects, the choice is yours whether to fall into the dark side or jump onto the bright side. Even in a dark situation, you have an internal light shining to guide you. However, it is essential to develop the muscle of self-awareness and an understanding of how to use it. It begins when you can commit that you are here to experience and cherish the celebration of every moment of your life, whether or not you perceive it as good or bad, right or wrong.

Did you know that one of the longest-running children's television shows in history is *Power Rangers*? Two men created a pilot (based on a successful Japanese television show) and it took them seven years to get anyone to believe in their idea. Wherever they went, they got rejected. They showed the pilot to anyone who was interested, and they were repeatedly laughed at and turned down. It seemed that Hollywood didn't believe in the power of teenage superheroes in spandex suits. Network executives thought it was the dumbest idea they'd ever seen. The creators knew the show was kind of crazy and wacky, but they believed in it. It was a live-action cartoon with a whole bunch of bizarre monsters. But they felt there was something very special about this show that they knew would spark the imagination of kids everywhere—because it sparked the kid in them.

All the networks and advertisers at the time turned it down, but the head of the new Fox Children's Network gave it a chance. The pilot of the *Mighty Morphin Power Rangers* premiered on Fox during the summer of 1993 and was slated for an eight-week run. The expectations were low, as school was out and most kids were on vacation. There were no mobile devices back then and kids had to sit in front of a physical television set to watch the series.

What happened next surprised everyone. The ratings went through the roof. The *Power Rangers* became a runaway hit and an overnight phenomenon, unlike anything that had come before. This show came from left field and appealed to the imaginations of children all over the world, who resonated with the music, the characters, and their stories.

After years of rejection—like what J. K. Rowling experienced with the *Harry Potter* books—there was one person who believed in what they were doing and wanted to join them on their crazy quest. It took one woman to unlock the potential of the *Power Rangers* television show, because she shared the vision. And it was the kids, not the advertisers or the TV network executives, who resonated most with it. The kids were the last group in the food chain to be asked for their opinion and the first to openly embrace the show.

These stories of "greatness" and "success" can be either incredibly helpful or soul crushing. A lot depends on what you truly want to create in the world and whether it comes from your whole being or from a need to be seen and recognized by an outside force. If you talked to the creator of *Power Rangers* or the *Harry Potter* series, you might be surprised by what you found, and a lot would depend on the questions you asked.

But the world toward which we are headed is unknown and is one where we can believe more in ourselves and not always wait for someone else to choose us for whatever we want to bring into existence. Our opportunity is to understand that the model of waiting to be picked is a limiting belief, which we explored in great depth in *F*ck the Bucket List for the Soul*. Sure, we need to have a healthy community and the care of others, but we also need to believe we are enough and have the capacity to create like never before. Prince Charming, Superman, and Wonder Woman are all fairy-tale characters, and life is real and waiting for you to experience it—no heroes required.

Each of us is on our own unique journey, and once we discover our own wonder and have the courage to trek into the unknown, we can begin to explore what's truly in our heart and find others who share our passion for whatever sparks us. It could be starting a garden or forming something to ignite the imagination of children. Though you believe in what you're creating, you'll meet many people who will laugh at you or judge you, and it will be up to you to keep going, by lifting yourself up and not taking on the fears of anyone else.

I love meeting heart-filled people with whom I immediately connect, not just through words but through what we are building in the world. Carol Chapman sees herself as a recovering corporate addict. She spent over twenty years in corporate roles, and they were some of the best and most challenging times of her life. Since she was a young girl, she was determined to make something of herself and, like so many of us, followed the traditional route to achieve celebrated success and happiness.

And she became really good at making something of herself—the way society defines it. She spent years climbing the corporate ladder until she became a senior executive at a global hospitality company operating, managing, and franchising some of the world's best-known hotel brands. Her family moved with her to Singapore, where she was the chief human resources officer in a region spanning twenty-two countries and twenty-five thousand employees. But after more than twenty years in the corporate world, her heart started whispering to her that life in this world wasn't all it was cracked up to be. This success was not as fulfilling and rewarding as advertised, and she was now in a position to trek into the unknown.

"Suffice it to say, over the years, I've had my fair share of ups and downs," shares Carol. "But who hasn't? Life can be a roller coaster. You can either ride head down, wincing and gasping with fear, knuckles clenched to the seat bar, *or* head up, embracing the ride with curiosity and enthusiasm, arms and hands reaching high and wide."

We each experience trauma in our lives. No one is spared, despite the fairy tales and the action hero movies we consume as children. For Carol, it started when her first-grade teacher ridiculed her in front of the entire class. And later in life, she lost parents and siblings to illnesses and suicide. She also suffered a life-threatening brain aneurysm and surgery at forty-five, which forced her to pause and reflect deeply.

Carol took the plunge and decided to explore life as an entrepreneur. "Life takes the needed turns when you least expect it. That could be good. That could be bad. It depends on your perspective," she shares. She ventured out and explored new things, like becoming a certified executive coach. She founded a company that helped organizations build their brands from the inside out. She codeveloped a methodology to uncover the unique DNA of an organization's brand and then published a book about it.

For many of us who choose the entrepreneurial route, our partnerships don't always work out, and Carol found herself dissolving an eight-year business partnership and friendship. She also spent five years of intense soul-searching for her purpose and meaning in life and learned that "the darkness doesn't linger forever but it sure feels like hell when you go through it!"

Today, Carol believes that the power to rise up is within, not outside of you. She has learned that being your best self takes time, just like developing a personal fitness routine that becomes a daily habit. It takes a healthy choice to get in shape and a lifelong commitment to stay in shape. Taking in all of her life's lessons, she met Christopher Drummond, her current business partner with whom she is unleashing her wildest creations and is excited about the Guided Meditation series they are creating to open up the hearts of anyone who experiences them.

Christopher is a recording and mix engineer, music producer, composer, sound designer, violinist, and Grammy Award voting member. He has composed and produced original musical scores for radio, television, and film. Christopher had his first "fuck it" moment when he was twelve years old. After completing his homework and doing all his chores (including mowing the lawn), he jumped on his ten-speed bike to go play with his friends. "My mother came out of the house asking me to stay home with her," he shares. "But I wanted to play and there was no reason for me not to go. That was the moment when I started to own my personal power and step out of the story of how a 'good' son should be."

Together, Carol and Christopher launched Hearts Rise Up, an online community and podcast, where they bring together impassioned consciousness warriors on a relentless quest for self-discovery, expanded awareness, and self-mastery. "Our community connects, shares, and supports each other in cultivating practices that create an intuitive, heart-centered life, so that we can realize true freedom. Releasing false beliefs, fear, and suffering allows us to live in the eternal present and become a light of unconditional love that heals and transforms the world by transforming ourselves."

The universe may be calling you to face your fears so they no longer have power over you. Perhaps what it is really asking of you is the willingness to let go of what has outlived its usefulness—because when you welcome death, you simultaneously open the door to birth. And when you embrace your imagination along with a hearty dose of courage, you will find yourself standing at the opening of a healthy path with the opportunity to transform yourself and your life. When you believe in what you are creating, you never give up on finding the person who can unlock the door on your path when you simply can't do it on your own. And you can also learn a lot about the power of rejection to help you keep going and believe in what you are creating in its purest form.

AN INITIATION TO QUESTIONING EVERYTHING

As part of our exploration, let's start by preparing the groundwork. Each one of us has a unique way of interpreting the world and much depends on not just our mindset—whether we see opportunities or challenges—but also how our heart responds to situations. Our societal conditioning, education, and past experiences all influence our overall frame of reference for how we see the world. Our frame of reference provides the context in which we make sense of day-to-day situations and decisions. Our beliefs ultimately guide the choices we end up making.

We each have a different frame of reference when we use words and language, which is why communication continues to be a struggle in so many relationships and situations. Say a friend invites you over for an "amazing" meal, and you dream about her famous vegetable curry all day, only to be served pork ribs and cauliflower soup with bacon bits. Not only are you disappointed because you assumed your friend knew what you loved and craved most, but also because she did not remember that you're highly allergic to cauliflower and don't eat meat. Someone may invite you on an "amazing" outdoor adventure, and you dream of a long walk on the beach but end up trekking through the desert. What's amazing to one person may not be so amazing to another. This is why questioning and becoming aware of the foundation of everything is so important. When a couple talks about their ideal living scenario, one person may envision building a castle while another is longing for a camper and a warm fire.

Develop an ability to question how you interpret anything, and question how that interpretation might be different for each of us. Where can you start? Below are some potential areas to consider, but please add and change as you see fit. Or you can skip this section and go to the next Expedition. This is your journey. Only you know what makes your heart tick.

Are you willing to go deep into your world?

If you feel called to do this, draw two columns. In one column write or draw what your **mind** is telling you is important in your life. Then write or draw in the other column everything your **heart** imagines you doing when no one is watching. Let it flow.

Capture everything as if no one else will ever see what is there. Don't censure or judge your answers. Take as long as you need to get a reflective picture of what wants to emerge.

Compare it with your observations about your limiting beliefs and conditioning, which we covered in the first two books. There is plenty to think about now, and it all boils down to creating balance between your mind and your heart, making sure that these two are in alignment with your real self, and becoming aware of places where they may be divided and those where they are aligned.

Can you question everything until it's meaningful for you?

Take a breath, move your body, shift your weight, or do whatever helps you feel deeply into your questions. When you look at what you captured in each column above, what jumps out at you? What questions pop up in your heart, especially when no one is judging you?

There is no doubt that the thoughts you entertain and the beliefs you hold strongly shape your life. That's why it's healthy to check in with yourself periodically to observe the kinds of thoughts that regularly take up residence in your mind and to tap into how your heart reacts. Are they constructive thoughts of hope, curiosity, and possibility, or destructive thoughts playing host to outrage, cynicism, doubt, anxiety, shame, victimization, and fear? Do you know where they originate? Are they your own or has someone planted them in you?

Your energy and power source helps you navigate throughout your life. Some people and things use up all your energy. Imagine that your energy is stored in a tank inside of your body. When you check the tank, are you running on empty or is your energy source fully powered? Take a hard look at what's working and what's not, because now is the opportunity to let go, purge, and cleanse in whatever way works for you.

If you have a bucket list, can you review it? If you don't, skip to the next question.

If you have a bucket list, please look at it and draw two columns on a piece of paper. In the first column, note the items on the list that fuel your soul and get you most excited. In the second column, note any items that you believe you *must* achieve before you die or ones you feel you're expected to cross off your list to be a successful person. Now, what's on your "fuck-it list"?

When you're ready, take an empty page. Write or draw everything your heart wants to experience in this lifetime; you can also leave some room for mystery. Now is the time to engage in activities that jump-start your soul and recharge your batteries. Like the technology you choose to bring into your life, understand how this list supports you.

And remember that without structure, without routine, and without lists, life begins to unravel. And that's okay when you're stepping into the unknown. Make sure that any list in your life supports you. If you have enough, now is the time to enjoy it.

What is pulling on your heart?

What are all the things that you've been putting off for someday when you have enough money, enough stuff, enough love, or enough time? Are you generous and kind with yourself? Do you know what makes you come alive? Where are the gaps and the alignment between your mind and your heart? What small steps can you take to gain an understanding of your blockages and your opportunities? What small steps can you take to become more aligned and whole?

The way forward may be to look at what your emotions are trying to tell you. Ultimately, living your life in your own way depends on your ability to follow the pull of your heart in understanding that when you're healthy, you can share your gifts with the world. There's something happening, as you will discover in this book and your own work, that is so much bigger than any of us.

Are you listening and tuning in to your soul?

If you are waiting for the world to tell you what is the "right" thing to do right now, you are going to be very disappointed and heartbroken. And yet, many of us have lost touch with our own internal guidance and have been taught to seek answers from the experts and gurus. We've been raised to expect an outside force or authority to know what's in our hearts. Your internal compass might say, "I know this is healthy for me. I'm going to trust this," or it may say, "That doesn't feel healthy to me." The question is, do you trust this internal knowing as a guide or wait for someone else to direct your life?

We live in a world that often tries to shut down our intuitive knowing. When we have a direct line to our heart, we access that rich fertile place where ideas, opportunities, and curiosity are found. By tuning in to your inner self and truly listening, whether it's noticing when you come alive or how you feel in a challenging situation, you will develop a stronger sense of who you are and what you want to create next.

Can you release anything that has served its purpose so you can regenerate your energy? Holding on to that which seems to want to leave your life is unhealthy and trying to control anything is usually pointless. True power comes from being willing to trust the currents and go with the flow, and this is your biggest opportunity as you listen to the whispers of your heart.

As you experience the Expeditions in this book, please add to them your observations and change whatever you need to. This life is yours to navigate with all you bring with you, and you can also leave stuff behind. There is no proven formula for how to be you—that's your ultimate job while you are here.

Imagine waking up in the morning and allowing yourself to be fully present by truly seeing and experiencing the beauty of our natural world. There is an excitement about learning more about yourself by trekking into the mystery of the unknown. You've never lived this day before and you never will again. Take the step you are ready to take, trusting that your path is unfolding. You may take a turn that you believe goes nowhere, and you feel anxious because you have been taught to see a mistake like this as a failure. You feel awful that you went the wrong way. But did you really?

Maybe it was a lesson in learning to let go of the manual you were given for how life should be lived. What if you tapped into your internal compass and had a long chat with yourself about why you felt a need to take this very turn? We are all on a journey of learning and growing. Can you see with a healthy heart what is really going on? Are your words aligned with your intentions and actions?

THERE IS NO DESTINATION—JUST LIFE

In our modern world, we are here to build community and connection, and to experience the magic that comes from seeing what stands in our way and then identifying opportunities for creation. Imagine a world of healthy, conscious creators of all ages and all walks of life deeply caring for ourselves and each other.

The more you realize that there's no need to "get there," the more life becomes a series of adventures and expeditions. With the awareness of what your heart is whispering, you make healthier choices about whether you want to live in fear or how much external noise you want to bring into your life. When you are health conscious, you get to decide how much entertainment, politics, business stress, and information you bring into your life and holistically evaluate what you're consuming and how it impacts your health.

Your heart usually knows when you're ready to take the first few steps. And once you do, nothing will ever be the same. You have choices: to stay in the current paradigm and fight for your life of "being right" or to step into the unknown. The deeper question concerns being aware of why you would *not* want to step out of the old toxic programming that may throw you into fear, outrage, blame, and hopelessness? What does being right or being in the right ever do for your well-being? What happens when you understand why you feed on something that is toxic to your well-being? Can you free yourself from the heavy baggage filled with limiting beliefs that you're carrying around with you, set them down on the road, leave them there, and never go back for them?

When you think about who you truly are, you don't need to define it by who you were. There's no going back to how things were—accepting some of the heartless way the world has been run when it comes to education, health care, politics, the way businesses operate. The decaying man-made world is filled with fear, division, poverty, addiction, depression, and never-ending wars and conflicts. The natural world is magical and beautiful. Once you start down the path and begin making healthy decisions about your life, you will look back at the old ways in disbelief and ask yourself, "How on earth did I live that way? And why?" It's natural to feel confused, lost, and uncomfortable at first. You were used to the false safety nets and life being a certain way. But a new path slowly appears as you let go of the unhealthy ways and limiting beliefs and take the first steps to open your heart to a healthy way of being.

It's not easy, because you will find yourself alone on an emerging timeline, leaving behind many who are still fighting for their lives and living in fear. There is a whole machine that was set up to keep us warring within ourselves and with each other, and there are people literally fighting to make sure that peace and unity never happen in our world. But what if your job is to focus on your own health and well-being, not to instruct others on what's best for them? Each of us is on our own journey and there are plenty of people on this journey with you. But you won't find us swimming in the status quo or mainstream.

What is ahead is a time for creation, for building healthy lives and communities. Our hearts are calling us to bring healthy structures to ideas and thoughts and creations—how we run our lives, our society, our companies, our economies, our governments, our environment, our education, and our health. Once we become healthy, we can listen to the whispers of our hearts that know deeply that what affects one affects all because we're all in different stages of readiness to explore possibilities.

You are here to get in tune with your heart, and everything is already abundantly here. Abundance is not something that has to be made new—it exists already, like the air you breathe. To tap into abundance, clear away what is not abundant. Unhealthy baggage and the need for winning at all costs are replaced by what supports your well-being. Toxicity is removed when you become aware of what and who is toxic in your life. A scarcity mindset is transformed when you can shift your mindset to see yourself as an opportunity creator. Fear, anxiety, pain, and anger are addressed when you do your own inner work. There's no going back when you're walking through a gateway of awareness. You can easily lead yourself into a healthy world of possibilities. You are already on your way if you're engaging with these books. The rest is in your heart and your ability to create.

Indigenous wisdom from Chiricahua Chief Cochise reminds us all that "you must speak straight so that your words may go as sunlight into our hearts ... I will not lie to you; do not lie to me."

EXPEDITION 21

WHAT'S IN YOUR HEART?

♥

When you trust your heart, you live as a courageous adventurer who is always trekking into the unknown, hatching healthy experiments, coming up with ideas, failing often, and converting your energy into kindness, compassion, and love for yourself, your community, and the planet. When you are health conscious, you become a dynamic creator of your life. You can no longer afford to sit back passively and complain or blame your problems on the world or anyone outside yourself. Why? Because you can no longer be satisfied with the world the way it is now. You consciously choose to step out of the stifling mediocrity of the mainstream and status quo of being told how to live your life. You want to come alive.

You are being invited to the biggest transformation on the planet today, but it's up to you to take the first steps. Is it time to unleash yourself like never before? Is it time to call on your curiosity and courage and trust life as you purge, cleanse, and release all that no longer serves you? Once you're in harmony and balance within yourself—physical, mental, and emotional balance—you can tinker and reset the harmony around you, trusting universal laws and the pure flow of life itself. Because only you control how you react to anything and everything. You will not change the external world by snapping your fingers or fighting your way through life. In times of transformation, and even crisis, you face an opportunity to reframe your situation instead of fighting it. You get to know that you are enough and when enough is actually enough. You can decide that you no longer need to be trapped in the ways you used to react; you can invest in learning to tap into your expansive courage to live a healthy life.

Imagination can drive the quality of your life. It gifts you the ability to envision opportunities and play with them through your creative spirit. Finding a way to tap into your intuition and imagination that works for you is a personal thing. It's a different process for each of us to learn how to stop whatever we are busy doing and invest our full resources into being in touch with our deep calling. As Dutch psychiatrist, author, and educator Bessel van der Kolk shares in his work on trauma and posttraumatic stress disorder (PTSD), "When people are constantly and compulsively pulled back into the past to the last time they felt deep involvement in deep emotions, they suffer from a failure of imagination, a loss of mental flexibility. Without imagination, there is no hope, no chance to envision" a healthy future, no place to explore, no reason to follow your heart.

When our dreams are big and we have a vivid imagination—like my dream of having millions and millions of people not only experience these books but come together as conscious creators—we will fail along the way. But we won't see it as traditional failure. We will become aware that it is the best education we will ever receive in how to be grounded in reality to see which seeds and ideas will bear fruit and which will rot.

You will ride your highs and lows with curiosity instead of letting fear ride you. You will be grounded in your own stories and take a plunge into uncharted waters when you are ready. And for me, imagining a world where more people reclaim their power to step into the unknown gives me hope that we can create something meaningful during our time on Earth and have a healthy relationship with ourselves and each other. Less suffering means more energy to be healthy and play. I envision these sparks of energy where we can ignite ourselves and each other in ways we never imagined.

Be willing to let both success and failure make equally important contributions to your life. After you allow yourself to appreciate the effort involved and the setbacks you've overcome, the next step you take can be even lighter—when you allow it to flow. Let your heart speak to you, and spend time imagining what you want to experience on your life's path; the gratitude when these events materialize can be overwhelming and very fulfilling. At the same time, you can be grounded in reality and understand your heartbreaks so you don't get stuck in the pain. Allow yourself to learn from the failures how to grow healthier relationships—from fertilizer, roses blossom!

LEAPING OUT OF CONFORMITY

Success is a very organic experience. Even world record holders cannot hold on to the climax of their euphoria for too long. There is always someone else around the corner waiting to challenge the record. Sustainable success comes in small doses. You can build one success on top of another and enjoy each small achievement until the next one comes around. Holding on to a successful experience cannot be a life goal. It would be like living on a small island, clinging to the one rock while the tides came and went. Eventually life would pass you by while you focused on keeping the nostalgic "win" alive.

Life is to be experienced, and not by seeing how fast you can check off a to-do list or get through someone else's manual of how you should live your life. Success is very personal. No two experiences are ever the same, and only you know what excites you and what breaks you. Some "thought leaders" talk about being fearless or limitless, but when you take into account your physical realities, there are definite limits you face. It's wise to look both ways when crossing the road and not walk into oncoming traffic; it's wise not to eat something that will make you ill. These types of fear are a natural part of being alive. But what *is* unhealthy is fearing that you are not good enough. Nature teaches us that there are shadows within the brightest lights—how you react to them is up to you. So, the question is, can you tap into your curiosity, imagination, creativity, and courage, as well as your rational doubt and fear, and be fully human?

When you are open to life, you learn more all the time. Your knowledge is constantly being updated through your experiences. Imagination helps you expand your body of knowledge and tap into your creativity. If you stop right now and look around your physical space at every object that surrounds you, notice that each one—whether a hat or a mug or a book or any material item—came out of someone's imagination. Each is a combination of an idea and a vision, mixed with a desire to create something in our world. The glass you use to drink your water or the cup you use to drink your favorite tea or coffee uses a technology that was created by a human being, just like a smartphone, virtual reality, or the latest cool gadget. Innovation is all around us and isn't just what lifts the stock market and makes shareholders financially rich. We have heart-filled people on the planet imagining the next wave of education, health, agriculture, food security, fashion, community, mental health, and so much more.

Years ago, a grandmother stood by a window awaiting a visit from her three grandchildren. A big smile appeared on her face when she saw them arrive. They were excited to see her too. Simon, the eldest, gave her a big hug and then the other two took their turns. She had prepared their favorite meal—dumplings with chicken—and they sat around the table chatting and eating. Hanna, the youngest, told her that they had some very exciting news. Their family's company was creating the first building with seven floors. "Can you imagine, Grandma, how many people can live in one place, and that we can now live in separate dwellings but still be together in one building?"

Grandma Rose, who had never seen a two-story home in her life, couldn't even imagine what they were talking about and wondered why on earth anyone would want to live that way. But she was excited for them and proud of their ability to envision another way of living that would benefit her family and community. As they dug into her famous peach pie, they celebrated the anticipation of a new way of living their family was birthing.

For nearly half a century, from 1931 through 1972, the 1,454-foot Empire State Building in New York City held the title of being the tallest building in the world. In the rankings of today's tallest man-made structures, the Empire State Building doesn't even make the top forty. The world's tallest building today, according to the Council on Tall Buildings and Urban Habitat, is the Burj Khalifa in Dubai, which soars 2,716 feet into the sky. Skyscrapers across Asia and the Middle East have been rising each year, with eight of the top fifteen tallest buildings in China. The human imagination is abundant with an ability to see beyond what already exists. When you tap into your imagination, you realize life is full of opportunities.

Γ IF YOU SAW OPPORTUNITIES
:AD OF PROBLEMS?

Not only are our internal stories loud, but the overwhelming amount of information and "news" we are bombarded with on a daily basis often prevents us from seeing opportunities. You may have been brought up to believe you should always stay informed. That is how the news programming works: they hook you. Media operates under the guise that people "in the know" will help you to be informed about whatever is "worthwhile" to know. News departments are mostly funded by advertising budgets, which influence what is deemed "newsworthy." As a former student of journalism and media, I learned to read between the lines and started to see both media (news) and medicine (illness) as thriving businesses for corporations.

Society teaches us to never appear ignorant or foolish. Ah, yes, that is the veil of reality. Knowledge, when you think about it, consists of information *and* misinformation. It is both, and it is increasing at a faster rate than ever before with instant news and social media platforms—which are more advertising platforms than truly social ones, as someone regulates what you are allowed to know. Remember, visibility and access to knowledge and materials is far more prevalent now than ten or fifteen years ago and keeps increasing in a world that values the quantity of content but not always its quality. It is almost impossible for anyone to "keep up" in today's world. And why do we need to keep up with the ever-increasing external noise and artificial intelligence (AI) algorithms that want to hook us into someone else's agenda? Have you ever stopped to think about how news benefits you in your own life? What's your relationship with information and being in the know?

When I was growing up, there was always a threat of war, and special codes were sent to the public through the media to let soldiers on reserve duty know when to mobilize and join their units. I listened to the news as a child because it impacted my very existence. I remember the three beeps coming over the radio when the news came on at the top of the hour, pouring out the latest headlines, telling us what we believed we needed to know. And when a war or terrorist attack took place, it was our sacred source of information.

I traveled around the world later in life and stayed plugged in to what was transpiring as much as I could. Having written my master's thesis on the impact of media on society, my own relationship with the news changed as I started to understand what was really going on with the ownership of media by big business. I went from being constantly plugged in to consciously connecting with people in different places through the Web to find out what was going on, instead of relying on a third party to broker my news. There are so many alternative sources popping up everywhere, like podcasts and local radio stations now accessible through the internet. You get to choose and tailor your listening to your own needs. Universal wisdom teaches us to go to the source of everything.

Imagine if you consciously decided to tune out of the external noise of our world. What would you need to stop doing and what would you consider starting? What does peace of mind mean to you? Remember, you're in control when you are the one who can choose whether to turn your devices on or off. The lighting in your dwelling doesn't go on automatically unless you have installed a device that automates it. Have you automated yourself?

One way I learned to cope is by not getting caught in the hamster wheel. What I mean by this is that a pet hamster is kept occupied with a treadmill wheel to stop it from becoming bored and destructive in its little box. It has proven to be a very successful tool—the hamster turns the wheel and runs until it is exhausted. As it runs, the wheel turns faster and faster, and the hamster has to run faster to catch up.

There comes a point when the wheel starts controlling the hamster's behavior and it becomes an addiction. Then, as with any addiction, the hamster is no longer in charge of its actions.

So instead of being caught in your hamster wheel, pay attention to whether you are in control of the wheel of life or if it's controlling you. You can step back and observe and become wildly open-minded and curious, or you can stay stuck running in the wheel. But at least be aware of the choice you are making. Massive amounts of organic information are already available when you are willing to get off the wheel and listen to what's calling you. The opportunity is imagining how you want to show up in your life and becoming aware of your own personal navigation system to make it a reality. It can be a messy but rewarding path. A car does not run without fuel or a charge. What fuels you to get to wherever you want to be?

BREAKING OUT OF ROUTINES

The goal of traditional schooling is to give children tried and trusted tools to build a successful life. The myth is that someone has your life mapped out, when, in essence, what you are mostly taught is to follow the rules and comply. You're taught to trust authority figures because they know what is best for you, and you get introduced to standards and norms that you're constantly measured against.

If you've worked at the same job for many years, you've most likely built your life around the demands of your work. You eat lunch at a certain time and take breaks along the way. You stop working at a certain time every day. You have daily interactions with others in specific ways tailored to fit your job requirements. If you suddenly and unexpectedly lost the job, these regular markers would disappear. There would be no need to get up at a certain time, eat at a certain time, and be back home at a certain time, and the people you interacted with for most of your waking hours would no longer be available to you. This situation is inherently disorienting, as your normal routine has disappeared.

But maybe this is also an opportunity to start questioning your work life. Are you allowed to ask for something different? The old way of life no longer satisfies your taste buds. You're bored with the same routine and want something else; you're hungry and know it's time to see what you can eat other than sandwiches. You yearn to change things, and you start to develop tools that help you understand what's needed to make it happen. You take the first step of this stage of the journey. You take time to explore your old path and your new possibilities. Your own intuition is waking up and starts talking to you. The question is, are you willing to listen, or is someone else's voice creeping into your story of how your life should be?

It was not unusual for people, centuries ago, to migrate. People did not just move from place to place because the water, food, and other resources were lacking where they lived. They simply had a feeling of restlessness and they tapped into their curiosity about what was up ahead, what was around the corner, or what was on the other side of the hill. In ancient times, there was little interest in building permanent structures but instead there was a curiosity to explore nature and imagine what was out there waiting. It is part of your basic nature as a human being to have a deep desire to discover the unknown. Everyone is at their own intersection, and the destination does not have to be a geographic location. You travel a lot more in your mind than you realize. You can do it right now, right here.

After you read the following paragraph, please close your eyes and let your words, images, and imagination flow into your heart. Have a pen, computer, notebook, sketchbook, or whatever works for you to write down or draw what comes in.

Imagine you are showing up in the world as the person of your wildest fantasy. Imagine what the world looks like when you do. Imagine how you want to show up. Now, close your eyes and imagine.

Open your eyes after you have imagined all the possibilities and all the impossibilities. Now that you're back:

- ♥ Where did you go?
- ♥ What did you see?
- ♥ How close or far is it from your current reality? Why?
- ♥ What is possible? Why?
- ♥ What is impossible? Why?
- ♥ What beliefs and routines do you need to let go of?
- ♥ Do the things you imagine stay in your mind as a fantasy for someday, or do you dare to make them happen with a full heart?
- ♥ What did you learn, if anything, about where you are and where you'd like to be?

Remember, this is not wishful thinking. Let go of time and your "to do someday" bucket list. Breathe and relax. Let go of control and allow whatever images want to show up. It takes practice to let go, sit, and be with your imagination. Many of us have been programmed to dream of beautiful, white sand beaches with palm trees and little umbrellas in our drinks. Yes, even our utopia has been programmed!

Go deeper—go even deeper where there is no programming. What's underneath? What drives your utopia? What do "sandy beaches and pretty cocktail drinks" represent? The opportunity and desire to relax, to be taken care of in beautiful surroundings. Yes, each of us wants to be loved and respected. No one wants an existence full of stress and suffering. If this is your reality, then isn't it time to dream of a healthier life that's yours? It will demand that you start to make some changes, especially in your thinking.

And it must be something concrete and real, or your dream will stay in the realm of wishful thinking. Unless you venture out and take steps, you will perpetually live in your imagination or in someone else's story of how life should be. In her book *Dreams*, South African author and visionary Olive Schreiner writes, "When love and life first meet, a radiant thing is born, without a shade. When the roads begin to roughen, when the shades begin to darken, when the days are hard, and the nights cold and long—then it begins to change."

MAKING CONNECTIONS THAT COUNT

If I had told you in 2007 that there would one day be a service where a stranger would pick you up in their personal car and take you to your destination, would you have thought it was too crazy to fathom? Could you imagine in 2011 that you would willingly get into a stranger's car—a stranger who already had your credit card information? Would you have believed that parents would find this service trustworthy enough to transport their children? And yet, someone did imagine it and then companies like Uber, Lyft, and many more were started. Today there is talk that in the future, windowless planes will give passengers a panoramic view of the sky. Instead of real-life views of the sky, the windows in a cabin will display screens, relaying a choice of views from around the aircraft. Someone is out there already imagining what our future experiences will be.

And would you have imagined that the humpback whale would come all the way back from the brink of extinction? Its population has returned to numbers it had attained prior to a period of whale hunting in the early 1900s. In the 1950s, there were only four hundred fifty humpback whales in the South Atlantic. That may seem like a lot, but the population had numbered twenty-seven thousand prior to the start of the twentieth century. And then humans began targeting them for their oil, and in just twelve years, between 1904 and 1916, twenty-five thousand humpback whales were killed. The killing continued until only four hundred fifty remained. In 1966, the International Whaling Commission took action to protect them by permanently banning commercial whaling, and a global effort was launched to help the whale population recover.

In Luc Besson's film *The Big Blue*, Italian free diver Enzo Maiorca is starting a dive in the warm sea off Syracuse. While in the water getting ready for his dive, he is talking to his daughter, Rossana, who is on the boat. He suddenly feels something hitting his back. When he turns around, he sees a dolphin. Initially, he thinks the dolphin wants to play, but he quickly realizes that it's trying to get his attention. Enzo follows the dolphin, and about twelve meters down, he sees another dolphin trapped in an abandoned net. He comes back to the boat and asks his daughter to join him. They both head down with their diving knives, and in a few minutes the dolphin is freed and emits what they describe as an almost human cry.

A dolphin can hold its breath underwater for up to ten minutes, then it drowns. The freed dolphin, still stunned, was guided to the surface by Enzo, Rossana, and the other dolphin. It blew foam and blood, and then it gave birth. The male circled them and, "standing" in front of Enzo, touched his cheek as if in a kiss or a gesture of gratitude. Then they swam away. Enzo Maiorca reminds us that "until humans learn to respect and dialogue with the animal world, we will never know our true role on this Earth."

When you do something healthy with pure intention, it ultimately comes back to you, and there is always a warm feeling and energy that is generated. It has nothing to do with your ego's need to be the best and everything to do with self-awareness and a connection to the universe. You are the conductor of your orchestra, you play the lead, and there are a number of other players to create harmony with.

Can you imagine what is possible when we lift each other up, instead of competing and seeking constant revenge on those who wronged us? When all you know is fighting, the story you experience is the oppressed becoming the oppressors—and we know how that ends every time, over and over and over again. Isn't it time to break free of these very real plotlines?

Martin Luther King Jr., the social activist who played a key role in the American Civil Rights Movement from the mid-1950s until his assassination in 1968, pointed out how connected we all are: "We are tied together in the single garment of destiny, caught in an inescapable network of mutuality. And whatever affects one directly affects all indirectly. For some strange reason, I can never be what I ought to be until you are what you ought to be. And you can never be what you ought to be until I am what I ought to be. This is the way God's universe is made; this is the way it is structured."

When you become aware of how connected everything in the world is, you will start thinking about the ingredients and energy you bring to every situation and every experience. Is there a point to feeling stressed and infusing that energy into your life? And what holds you back from feeling that you can also infuse fun and play into every aspect of your life? Fun, creativity, and self-expression can become more pronounced, encouraging you to do more of what you love and less of what you don't. You can commit to a creative project, generate more true connections in your life, or simply do more of what you enjoy. The drive to express yourself in a more authentic manner will increase—so anyone trying to squeeze you into a box had better watch out. When something no longer fits—a job, relationship, situation, sandwich, or way of being—it will be difficult to keep pretending. The more you embrace your true self, the more that is possible.

We can each learn to simply listen to our heart that tells us we can trust our own heartbeat when we truly feel it. This ability is abundantly available to every person on the planet. Feel free to ask it questions, but also respect it by being fully in tune with what it is whispering to you. Once the whispers become clearer, you can listen to it as quietly or as loudly as you prefer. And if something is stopping you, invest the energy to understand where fear or worry stem from so you can assess the root cause, and then listen some more. Your schooling may have taught you to think logically, but *your* truth never lies.

EXPEDITION 22

ARE YOU MAKING HEALTHY CHOICES?

♥

Throughout history, people have prophesied the end of the world. As far back as 2800 BCE, an unknown Assyrian prophet wrote on a tablet that the Earth "is degenerate in these latter days. There are signs that the world is speedily coming to an end." Many people today also believe that our world is in one of its darkest times and on the verge of collapse. But why would the collapse of a world filled with fear, hate, anger, blame, loneliness, depression, division, and conflict not be healthy and timely? Who truly wants to be a puppet in someone else's power struggle, suffering throughout life? Why do we need to suck it up and accept the status quo when it is unhealthy for most of us? Where does the deep-seated fear of change originate? And how can we unleash the energy of creation and take back our power, individually and collectively?

While massive attacks are playing out on the global stage and in our environment, more of us are looking to expand our imagination of what is possible and deepen our understanding of ourselves. It takes courage, energy, and massive curiosity to figure out whom to trust in today's world, relating to the beliefs we hold, the food we consume, and the people we listen to. Who do you trust to deliver on a promise? What information is trustworthy? What is real and what is fake? And how much do you trust your own decisions versus being told what is best for you by an outside authority?

IT STARTS NOW

Despite all that we know or hear, we might be living in the best of times. First of all, we're here, right now. We can become aware of the impact that our fast-food, disposable culture has on the environment, and we can examine our own habits and role in it. We can criticize the fact that a cup of toxic fast food—like French fries, for example—costs a dollar and a cup of healthy fruit costs five dollars, or we can understand that we created this pricing through what we value and are willing to pay for. As long as we'll pay eight dollars for a cup of designer coffee, the price will continue to rise, because each choice we make validates how much we're charged and are willing to pay.

Kentucky Fried Chicken cut healthier options from its menus after "no one" bought them. The chain tried three times in the last decade to introduce menu items that were less calorific and even spent £8 million installing ovens in its outlets in the United Kingdom. But they found that the customer coming into KFC is looking to consume the greasy chips; the health-seeker would not choose KFC as a place to eat.

There are many imaginative people experimenting with alternative fuels that do not deplete or poison the environment and making products that have natural ingredients that don't cause cancer. Each of us can become aware that we can make different choices when it comes to our health. It all starts with trusting in your own ability to live a healthy life. There is so much you can do to make an impact, as you can move and shift with unprecedented speed and take control of your decisions and how you react. More than a millennium ago, the Mayan civilization collapsed, partly because of the environmental crisis they caused. They did not know how to transform and were trapped in a situation they had created but did not know how to get out of.

Today, we have the wisdom to know that filling our oceans with plastic and polluting our air and drinking water is unhealthy for all of us. We have the knowledge to make healthier choices and stop trusting those who contribute to poor choices for humanity and the planet in the name of profitability. More people are focused on finding trusted connections, meaning, and a healthy way of life. We're witnessing the breakdown of many systems, and yet we're also more connected than ever. When you look for them, you will find many stories of people creating sustainable products in a circular economy that offers holistic solutions to anyone ready to live consciously.

In years to come, you will see much from visionary, conscious leaders like Shamini Dhana and her company, Dhana Inc., in deeply transforming our relationship with fashion in sustainable ways. Shamini is passionate about the outdoors and has represented Singapore in badminton, played collegiate tennis, cycled the world, and climbed the Himalayas. She brings to the fashion world over twenty years of experience in international strategy, global operations, venture capital, and executive leadership in corporate America. As a consultant, government foreign direct investment specialist, and banker, Shamini gained extensive experience in leading global business missions. But her true passion and purpose were expressed when she launched her own company, Dhana Inc., which empowers youth to connect to people and the planet through the medium of fashion.

In her article "What You Value, You Protect," she shares:

"This time has given us a period of respite to examine what truly matters to us—family, friends, community, health, exercise, the environment, nutrition, culture, clothing, technology, and travel. Understanding why it matters and how to value it is as important. For we protect, invest in, serve, direct our energy toward and spend valuable resources on what we value.

Memories are a special gift in life—they represent a connection to the present moment, which is an expression of our being, our connectedness to all life. If memories are to be treasured, then moments are to be lived. How we treasure our memories can be demonstrated in many ways. Every day we place a piece of garment on ourselves that has the power to connect to people and planet. Today, we have the ability to wear our values through fashion. This is what Dhana stands for—an offering to connect to people and planet through the medium of fashion. With Dhana's Circular Fashion Collection, I invite you to reconsider your clothing as something representing memories and values waiting to be celebrated and shared with the world."

There are many people today, of all ages, working on the edges, not the mainstream, to come up with alternative paths and ways of living that can unleash our passion and breathe new life into our world. Our focus is on increasing our wisdom in how to live consciously and regenerate the earth. Visionaries like Joe Brewer are connecting us back to the land. In his essay "The Survivors Will Be Bioregional," he writes:

"I invite all who read this essay to walk open eyed into the dark night of your soul. Are you dead sunlight re-animated by burning fossil fuels that will walk steadfast into collapse unaware of your true condition in this larger pattern? Or will you learn to see that a pattern of thriving can be found that is far from your perceptions of normal in these extremely bizarre and unprecedented times that all of us were born into? I do not ask these questions lightly. My wife and I chose with eyes wide open to birth a child. Our daughter is going to turn four in a few months. And we are doing all that we can to organize our lives around a bioregion in serious need of regeneration in the Northern Andes of Colombia where we have recently staked a claim in the land and call this our new home ...

We know how to build water retention systems. There are local people who protect and propagate native plants. A reforestation effort began ten years ago in the Móncora Bioparque that is a community food forest and teaching ground for the people who will take on this vital work. Many of the campesino farmers have already organized themselves into cooperatives so they can help each other survive. A rich culture of earthen construction, use of natural fibers to make baskets and clothing, and other aspects of subsistence living remain intact here in this remote mountain town. We can see inklings of survival for these people who raised their children a generation ago during the 57 year civil war that wrought violence upon Colombia and made it far easier to extract local wealth while the locals themselves were too poorly organized to stop it from happening. Hold to the honesty of what history reveals. Let the science of ecology show you the way. Become bioregional or die. This is a stark choice that most of us will not consciously learn how to make. Onward, fellow humans."

There are abundant stories of remarkable people in our world who are charting healthy paths, and you will rarely hear about them in mainstream news. But these visionaries are simply doing their best to live their truth. Another example is Oniya, a beautiful sanctuary and biodynamic farm in southern Colorado, which is now being built to activate our connection with Nature and Unci Maka (Grandmother Earth). The thirty-seven acres, attached to thousands of acres of BLM managed lands, lies along La Jara Creek and is home to antelope, elk, bear, beaver, lynx, mountain lions, ermine, hawks, and eagles. The reintroduction of bison is a vital part of Oniya's mission and vision to heal the soil and share biodynamic practices for local and global soil restoration.

Oniya is the heart child of Tara Sheahan, cofounder of Conscious Global Leadership, Breathelab, and Where Bison Roam. After being diagnosed with Lyme disease in 1998, Tara began working with renowned Ayurvedic practitioners and neuroscientists, using breathwork and meditation to support her healing from chronic illness to full recovery. She was eventually able to manifest her dream of cross-country ski racing in the 2006 Winter Olympic Games at age forty-five—and, within two years, she was among the top ten ski racers in the country.

Tara is now on to a new dream of building a space for heart-centered people to gather. The Medicine Wheel Teaching Center is made of locally sourced adobe bricks. When completed, the structures will be powered with solar and wind energy. She is also part of a new collaboration, Makho Cheya, which means "Our Earth We Love Sincerely" in the ancient N/DN/D/Lakota (Sioux) language. Her dream is to re-wild and restore to balance the microbiome of Grandmother Earth's soil.

I am sharing these stories in the hope that you take action. I want to ignite a dream in you to create something healthy in your own life or to feel hope that we do have amazing visionaries and creators in the world. You can reach out to any of them to learn more and get involved. You hold the power of unlocking your own heart and trusting yourself. You no longer need to wait for someone to choose you.

IT'S ALWAYS A CHOICE

There is much we can imagine when it comes to how we choose to live our life. We can be trapped in an unhealthy state of mind where all we experience is doom and gloom, or we can imagine what is possible. Please be specific with your intentions; get down to the nitty-gritty, even when it makes you feel a bit uncomfortable. The areas of discomfort are the ones calling for your attention, as they will teach you everything you need to know about what's holding you back. When you experience resistance, you will know there are unresolved blockages to be acknowledged and addressed. Can you find forgiveness from past mistakes so you can let them go and make space for trusting that you have learned from them? Back then, you may not have trusted yourself to make the healthiest decisions, and you may have chosen relationships and work positions that were flat-out toxic for you. You can easily tap into the past as a reference point for a current lack in yourself.

Once you acknowledge the areas where your trust is broken, you can start understanding them and make space for healthier things and people to show up in your life. The key is to begin to unleash your curiosity and see where it takes you. It all comes back to self-awareness and self-care—two key elements we never learn about at mainstream schools. The opportunity to learn, shift, and grow only happens when you trust yourself and choose to trek into the unknown.

Can you imagine a world where people adopt an opportunity mindset and create with vivid colors? Do you trust that the rest is simply noise and distraction to keep you chained to a world of never-ending consumption? What kind of world do you want to create from a balanced mind and heart, in harmony and unity? Isn't it time to truly embrace your own ability to lead and own it? No blaming or judging needs to be packed for this adventure. If we created the fast-food culture and the separation that envelops our collective mindset, we can also create and lead with trust, compassion, and integrity.

Although it's obviously not true in all cases, when you stop to talk to a homeless person on the street of any city in the world or talk to a teenager living in a slum, you may have the opportunity to learn a great deal. You will often find that they don't want your charity and they don't trust your intentions. I can't speak for each person, but what I have learned from the ones my friends and I have connected with is that they want opportunities and help imagining the possibilities of what they can create in the world, like everyone else on the planet. Despite being financially poor, they are rich in so many ways, especially in knowing how to trust themselves. And many no longer trust that a nonprofit has their best interests at heart. They only give their trust to those who partner with them rather than try to save them. No one wants to be saved or fixed. Most people want to be seen and to live in dignity.

We're at a crossroads right now and have an opportunity to write healthy stories to regain our humanity. We can no longer wait. It is going to take a few outliers—like Magatte Wade, CEO and founder of Skin Is Skin—with the ruthless courage to go out there and say, "I'll do it even if my life is on the line." Even if only a few of us succeed, we will break through. There are millions of people standing behind us waiting for the doors to open. You may not know they are there, but they are silently watching and waiting.

It is a messy, messy world. And yet, there is a lot of hope. That's what keeps Magatte going. She believes that the poor are not always poor because they choose to be. Microfinancing is better than doing nothing, but many people don't have an understanding of the holistic system. Any society that has made it from poverty to prosperity had to rely on small and medium enterprises to get there. They are what create the jobs. In a new economy, there will be new types of jobs. But at the end of the day, people need to find ways to make money so they can provide for themselves and their basic needs. A lot of us in the West have created what Magatte calls a "thatchwork ceiling" (as opposed to a glass ceiling). There's excitement for people to buy from co-ops in the developing world, but no one is pushing it further. It's time to move things vertically, where vertical markets connect businesses around their specific needs so that people can learn better skills that have more value.

Magatte asks you to think about this question: What is the world excited about when it comes to Africa? On the one hand, we're excited about microfinance, and we're pouring trillions of dollars into it. To do what in the end? People are staying below the poverty line. It really hasn't done much. There is data that supports this. According to microfinance recipients' responses in surveys, more than 85 percent say they'd rather have decent jobs if given the choice. On the one hand, you have microfinancing mobilizing so much money and energy, and on the other hand you have multinationals who have access to the bond markets and private equity funds. And we know that neither actually creates jobs. In the middle, there is nothing, and there are not many job creation programs.

What if we created jobs for all the people who got microfinancing and gave them stability and an opportunity for a healthy life? The documentary *Poverty, Inc.* shows that the poor are often poor because of how these regions are regulated. People in poverty need their own incomes, which come from employment. We need to create better ecosystems for job creators.

Magatte's own village in Senegal is a mecca for artisan shoemakers. Right now, it's giving hundreds of people a livelihood, selling to the local community. It feeds those who work there. Imagine that village's worst-case scenario: All of a sudden, a TOMS Shoes truck shows up with a bunch of free shoes. It would put the local artisans out of business (and every TOMS copycat has the potential to do the same thing).

As *Poverty, Inc.* addresses, the primary reason Africa is poor is not because Africans don't have enough stuff, nor is it because Africa hasn't received enough aid or charity. Magatte shares in interviews and her blog that the main reason many Africans are poor is because they lack the institutions of justice that would enable them to create prosperity for themselves. Celebrities don't help by reaffirming ignorant stereotypes of Africa as a barren, dependent, hopeless continent. In Bob Geldof's case, he could've made a stronger positive impact by focusing on singing about property rights, rule of law, justice in courts, and entrepreneurship—making those concepts sexy and popular to those who wouldn't care otherwise. Magatte suggests that everyone watch *Poverty, Inc.* to get a glimpse of how the common idea of helping Africa can actually hurt the African people.

Becoming health conscious takes courage because it forces us to realize how much we don't really know. Africa should not be a problem to be solved by any outside force. We need to stop approaching everything with a problem-solution mindset and the belief that we have the answers to issues we know nothing about. Even with the highest degree of empathy, an outsider cannot know what it's like to live in Nairobi, Kibera, Nigeria, Senegal, or South Africa.

Moving forward, once we know ourselves, we can know what we would like our environment, our culture, and our well-being to be like. We can engage in dialogue with our youth and elders, be on the land, connect with nature, and listen deeply to what is healthy for us. We can ask for help from outsiders but not allow them to overpower us with whatever they believe is the best solution for us, when they don't know us. In the words of author James Baldwin, "Not everything that is faced can be changed, but nothing can be changed until it is faced."

THE HUMAN SPIRIT IS INCREDIBLE

Austrian psychiatrist and Holocaust survivor Viktor Frankl is a timeless testament to the luminous tenacity of the spirit. "Everything can be taken from a man but one thing: the last of the human freedoms—to choose one's attitude in any given set of circumstances, to choose one's own way," he writes in *Man's Search for Meaning*. While some people proclaim that this is the era to search for purpose and meaning, I believe it is not so much the search but our ability to see ourselves and connect in purposeful ways.

Is it utopian to believe that we're on the verge of an evolution of the human spirit, for those of us ready to trust ourselves and create healthier paths? When we look at the world today, we can see that in some areas, we're freer than we've ever imagined. For example, in a span of just fifty years, women have gained more freedom in many countries. And yet, so many things have not truly changed when it comes to equality, justice, and quality of life. Many of us are reevaluating who we trust as we witness human history repeating itself with the same plotline of corrupt politicians and leaders, magnate-controlled media, and elitism ruling society. Some of the most popular science fiction and apocalyptic zombie movies paint a haunting picture of our collective evolution. If we can do all this, isn't there an opportunity to believe that we can also paint a picture of the healthy life built on abundant trust in oneself, meaningful work, and shifting from being a consumer to being an adventurer and creator?

You can be sure that people will continue to dream up utopian projects. But if those projects are just the latest fad they want us to consume so their sales and wealth will increase, we won't be able to trust them. A 2018 MIT research study found that, in today's busy world, people are 70 percent more likely to share "fake" news, especially when it includes images and pictures. The simple act of repeating a story can make it seem like the truth, and all we do throughout life is create and exchange stories. Millions of people are becoming increasingly aware that we have been sold a dream that is at odds with our true potential. It may have broken our trust in the system and we may not know who to trust anymore. We can turn off the news or cancel our cable TV subscription, but the noise of the world will continue to march on until we embark on a conscious and healthy path.

It is easy for people to tell you how to live your life and offer specific steps to success, but do they really know you? Do you truly know yourself? If your answer to these questions is yes, you may want to stop reading and go do something else. But if you want to explore more deeply, take as much time as you need to identify a few areas where you have been conditioned to believe there is a particular "right" path for you. Then ask yourself: "Who do I trust? Who trusts me? And what fosters this trust? Are there any limiting beliefs or a memory that is holding me back? Why do I need to hold on to it?"

It takes a lot of practice to balance perfectly upon the tightrope of trust. One tiny doubt creeps in and you may teeter and fall. But when you learn to trust your heart, and make it a habit, everything is taken care of. You learn to question everything as you learn that when you are running too fast or desperately searching in an unhealthy direction, you get embroiled in someone else's story.

If your current reality is starting to crack and doesn't work for you anymore, you may be experiencing a shift in perspective that is preparing you to create something new and healthy. When you can work through your challenges, you can shine a light on how much transformation and growth you are capable of achieving. When you pull away from mainstream self-judgment of good and bad, you become increasingly aware of what works for you and what doesn't.

So why invest precious time and energy in judging whether your past decisions were good or bad, when your opportunity is to become aware of what and who is unhealthy in your life so you can adopt healthy practices and find trustworthy people? Facing your own self-judgement allows you to free yourself from the constant "sentencing" that has jailed you. What are the simple mistakes and misunderstandings in your life that have caused you to stay in a state of suffering, locked behind invisible prison bars?

Your opportunity is right here. You have the ability to push the boundaries of your evolution by truly experiencing all of life. There are no mistakes. You are awarded many life lessons, and how you approach them is personal; they are *your* lessons to learn. When you break down boundaries, you are clearing the foundational path and learning why trust is so critical on your journey. You are making space for healthy, fresh elements that are attuned to who you are and how you want to show up in the world.

Despite popular belief, there is no destination on life's journey. You never really need to find yourself—you are already here. What you learn in the school of life is that you can create yourself, not through passively waiting for someone to choose you, but through thousands of actions, healthy and unhealthy, practiced in every waking moment. To become self-aware, you don't need to get away from it all, just take the opportunity to face it all, in your own time.

It's up to you whether you medicate, meditate, or explore your own path in order to evolve. No one has your answers.

It takes work, and at some point, we make a sacrifice of our old self to emerge aligned to our true nature and to nature itself. The process of transformation is a death and a birth. They are one. They are interconnected in flow. The Zen Japanese term *shoji* means "birth-death." There is no separation between life and death other than a hyphen that connects the two. We cannot truly be alive without being aware of death. Death is always with us, helping us to discover what matters most and serving as a teacher of letting go. When we experience rebirth, we understand that we're not here on our own and that we can cocreate with all the resources around us in community.

CAN YOU TRULY TRUST YOURSELF?

During your lifetime, you can expand your ability to deepen your relationship with yourself. Trust is one of the foundations of being human. When you're faced with uncertain times, it's an opportunity to observe how much you trust or mistrust yourself. There is always another path to take when you're ready to question and do your inner work.

For many of us, our lack of trust stems from blaming ourselves or some outside force for what's happening in our lives and the external world. We each carry a sense of self-betrayal; no one is spared. We might also feel that a person or an institution or system has let us down and broken our trust. And yet, we often forget that when we feel this way, it is an opportunity to understand whom and why we trust. It could be some deep trauma or wound from when we were victimized, or even ancestral trauma that we've inherited (we covered this in the first book). It might also be a limiting belief carried in our baggage wherever we go, a belief that clutters the hallways of our hearts.

The first step is awareness. That is what being conscious is all about: being aware of root causes and taking a deep look into our foundation to see what trust means to us and how trust or mistrust has shown up for us. This energy flows through our veins, and our ability to understand where it stems from, and who is actually trustworthy for our well-being, is foundational.

Most of us have been raised to trust authority figures—whether it's a parent, a teacher, a religious leader, or a boss—before ourselves. We've been conditioned by society that someone outside ourselves is trustworthy. And life has shown many of us that it was not always wise to follow this instruction. Not everyone is healthy for us. Not everyone can know what's right for us, even with the best of intentions.

True freedom is experienced by unleashing our full potential and going deep into the corners of our mind so we can free it from the known. I hope these words that were entrusted to me can help you find practical ways to develop your personal power. The universe is here to give whatever level of push you may need, so you can move forward in the direction you feel called to take.

When you choose to let go of the blame or sense of being let down, you can locate a source of trust within yourself. Otherwise, you spend your life forever seeking justice for betrayal. Ask yourself, "Where does my mistrust stem from? Where do I feel that I have been betrayed by myself, and by the people in my life? Who do I become when I feel betrayed and mistrust everyone, including myself?"

You will not change the world by fighting against the current systems but by creating a vision of what could be and remembering to trust yourself as a powerful creator. When you focus on a healthy vision, trust becomes an ever-present reality constantly expanding your experiences. When you perceive your past as a mistake, you are constantly giving energy to this belief. Universal law teaches that there are no mistakes, only lessons and reflections along your path. You can then become aware of the root cause of your feeling of betrayal or loss of trust, which will help you integrate and take action.

And along the way, some people will disappoint you. If you are stuck in the limiting belief that people know what's right and good for you, you will most likely be let down. Trusting yourself and creating trusted relationships are the gateway to living a healthy life. It's not necessary to remain stagnant in relationships that uphold false identities for the sake of safety. You can work through challenging people and experiences by not getting sucked into their drama or wanting to fix them.

Although revealing your truth in some situations may seem difficult—such as deciding whether a relationship is healthy or toxic—it's worth the effort, as there is more joy, peace, and abundance to be uncovered. Your willingness to evolve in love with others is the precursor to more love evolving within humanity.

And please remember, being safe is very risky when you are caged in your limiting beliefs. How can you explore unknown opportunities and possibilities when you're stuck in your comfort zone and a false sense of safety? This is why understanding who you trust and mistrust—including yourself—is foundational. Any emotion you have that bubbles to the surface is an opportunity to get to the root cause and examine why you feel sad, anxious, burned-out, or playful and joyous. I sometimes find myself feeling very sad for humanity and know that there is internal healing I need to do so I can fuel and create the life I desire, rather than bringing destruction or fear into my life. I am sure there are millions of people who have experienced this feeling. I like to imagine what can happen when we each do our own inner work with gentleness and self-care to release our hurt and pain. When you can learn to stop fighting yourself and those around you, you are gaining the ability to create your own peace.

Can you trust yourself, open your heart, and get on your purposeful path? Sometimes the only love that exists is the one you create for yourself. If you are reading this, you're most likely one of the courageous visionaries our world needs right now. You may be ready to put down your sword because you understand that in the world we're creating there's no reason to war within ourselves or with others. "An eye for an eye" simply keeps us divided and blind. Martin Luther King Jr.'s energy joins us here: "It really boils down to this: that all life is interrelated. We are all caught in an inescapable network of mutuality, tied into a single garment of destiny … Whatever affects one directly, affects all indirectly. I can never be what I ought to be until you are what you ought to be. This is the interrelated structure of reality."

EXPEDITION 23

THE UNIVERSE IS ASKING
YOU TO GET REAL

Throughout my life, I have been able to identify trends and see what people will follow. Maybe it's because I studied political behavior and journalism, and I started my professional career in market research. I was trained to gather the opinions of massive numbers of people and make sense of them. Through statistical analysis, I learned to identify the mainstream opinion, and, on my own, I could also see the edges of humanity as well—the people who fell outside the normal distribution and status quo. I listened in on hours of interviews with people and built into the questionnaires ways to identify how people contradict themselves in their own minds.

In my late twenties, I was running the national public opinion polls for the national newspaper in Canada, and with a brilliant team we designed a rolling daily poll to capture people's opinions before a referendum. One day the prime minister, Jean Chrétien, sent the editor of the newspaper a note telling him to fire his pollster, because he felt the numbers were off. After the official results were released, our polls came in within 1 percent of the official vote. The editor sent the prime minister a note saying that he should now send his pollster flowers and apologize.

Well, that never happened, so I got involved with the Consumer Confidence Index survey for the Conference Board of Canada and learned even more about how our opinions and beliefs create part of our reality. It was so simple that it amazed me that most people couldn't see what was really going on. The possibility of unifying the physical with the power of the mind was astonishing. But there was also the dark side where I first experienced the level of manipulation of marketers, advertisers, bosses, and politicians who were in the business of power, financial growth, and never-ending expansion and success.

I learned to see how trends start and the power of celebrity in people's lives. I have had a front row seat to identifying trends and seeing them explode and go big. "Big" meaning they went mainstream and everyone attached themselves to the latest and greatest trend because some powerful force told them it was cool and what they needed. A recent example of going big is the growing New Age industry, which has emerged from the big business of spirituality. You may or may not be familiar with it, but it is out there.

This world is filled with more gurus and self-appointed spiritual teachers than we know what to do with. CEOs now have meditation coaches, monks, anthropologists, futurists, philosophers, and shamans on their payroll. Many business leaders have started mindfulness programs, offering yoga and meditation to their stressed-out and burned-out employees without addressing why people are so stressed and anxious in the first place. There are more workshops and books on how to manage conflicts and build diverse teams than on how to be an effective communicator and community builder. And which do we need most at this point in history—more conflict resolution or more meaningful connection, communication, and community building?

JUMPING INTO THE DEEP END

As a very stressed-out employee myself, I heard about mindfulness in 2007 and went to conferences in San Francisco and New York City in 2012, where experts were paraded out and streamed into our consciousness as having "the answer." I was told that technology was my enemy—which was amusing, as one of these events was held at the Google headquarters in New York City—and that I needed to sit quietly and detox from technology, to be present. It was the birth of the mega spirituality business in the West; this conference of a few hundred people is now a very big business around the globe. It created new heroes and best practices for "doing it right," and people were hungry for what was being offered. We all wanted some nirvana.

When I experienced all this blaming of technology for my burnout and was told that our entire society suffered from attention deficit hyperactivity disorder (ADHD), I was confused. Technology is not evil. It all depends on how we use it and integrate it into our lives. We can't blame technology or television or social media, for example, for not knowing when to turn the volume up or down in our own life. We can use technology without allowing it to use us. It's that simple. As I listened, what I heard was that technology was bad and unjust, and there was no mention of or conversation about the root cause of our situation. Telling us to sit quietly, meditate, and do yoga does not encourage us to understand what is truly causing our suffering. Being told to go inside myself and remember who I was felt like just more mumbo jumbo to me at the time.

And when I asked questions, I felt like an outsider in a secret society—much like the way I have always felt in the world itself. At no point was there meaningful dialogue about the real suffering people are experiencing and that personal stress originates from being overworked, taking on too much, working three jobs to pay the bills, or being in abusive relationships. At the same time, teen suicide was skyrocketing, human trafficking was out of control, and burnout, not greed, was categorized as a mental health issue by the World Health Organization.

Being told to sit on a cushion in silence and go inside yourself to find your answers only makes the person selling the trendy new cushions richer. It also extinguishes your power and desire to openly question what is truly going on. It was like being back in school, where you were either with the "in" crowd and the cool kids or the unpopular outsiders. But since I had played this game before in school and at work, I opted to be the curious outsider and observer before following blindly—although sometimes I immersed myself in the full experience to feed my curiosity.

My theatre training became practical in the theatre of the world we constructed. The people around me were simply doing their best. They were not bad people. Some were just not healthy for my well-being. But the message I kept hearing was that the source of my stress was inside my head or caused by digital technology. Other cultural and economic influences were not openly considered unless they were gender related or involved the death of capitalism and the approaching Age of Aquarius, and how everything will be better when the "woke" ones will move into the higher vibrational dimensions and the Fifth Dimension.

THERE'S ALWAYS HOPE

Along the way, I did meet firsthand some amazing people who were creating breakthrough solutions for veterans, PTSD, and end-of-life therapy—people who ranged from US Congress members and Buddhist monks to leading global scientists and researchers. I saw programs launched to help people lead healthier lives. I met people dedicated to providing new forms of natural therapy and healing through Stan Grof's Breathwork. I learned a great deal from dinner conversations with Stan and from his book *Beyond the Brain*, where he writes that "Western science is approaching a paradigm shift of unprecedented proportions, one that will change our concepts of reality and of human nature, bridge the gap between ancient wisdom and modern science, and reconcile the differences between Eastern spirituality and Western pragmatism." There were many people doing amazing work that matters in people's lives all in their own silos. I also witnessed the endless internal conflicts between organizations that were trying to help veterans or make the end of life less painful and more gentle.

And even in the "mindful communities" the battle lines were drawn around who would get the most funding, the most recognition, and the most mindshare. For me, it was simply sad. I wanted to take the people I was meeting into a room and have a very frank conversation about how much veterans and people with PTSD, for example, needed them to work together and not get stuck in the same sick, competitive frameworks that caused all this suffering in the first place. Maybe I was a bit delusional to hope that when we focused on health and well-being, the people who needed support would benefit?

Living and working in the Silicon Valley, I saw the mindfulness movement expand as so many people were seeking answers to the fast-food franchise culture we found ourselves in. There were gurus happy to have you listen to their prescriptions for how to "find nirvana," "remember who you are," and "walk you home." Silent meditation retreats and visits to ashrams in exotic places were skyrocketing, as well as the latest weekend psychedelic journeys for those with the financial means to partake of this expanding industry that was spreading like wildfire in the Western world. Through the ages, shamans have been called by spirits to heal bodies, minds, and souls— but the current reality has been calling some of them to the dark side of the spiritual business. Was it unnatural or a bit insane for me to overhear a "shaman" talk about how he plans to become a billionaire and make more money than his father?

People around me were blowing wide open with little or no integration into day-to-day reality, buying more and more of the medicine and enlightenment that was for sale. This is a fact and there is no judgment here. I learned that whatever we choose to do takes us on a path to the lessons we are meant to encounter. Again, pure and sacred practices are beautiful and can help tremendously along the way; it is when they reach the status quo—the mainstream—that you can question whether or not they are healthy for you. You can feel the energy in your body telling you whether something or someone resonates with you. It is personal and there is no one-size-fits-all approach to dealing with whatever you want to deal with.

But rather than fulfilling my intention of connecting with other creators, my world seemed to unravel more and more. While I wanted to believe that people were doing their best, I learned that what's best for them was not always best for me. I started paying more attention to their foundation and seeing whether it was whole and intact or whether they were trying to sell me their broken pieces. While selling spirituality was the name of the game of this estimated four-billion-dollar business, the opportunity I saw was to be spiritual by not taking anyone else's prescriptions. I did not want to become more skilled in navigating the rat race with the same practices that created the original rat race. I wanted a way out of the race and to become part of a community that wanted to cocreate the bridges to a healthy world.

I wondered how I had stumbled into this world, when I was simply hoping to connect with people who were interested in finding another way out of the craziness of the constraining frameworks that existed around us. Sure, I had questions, but I was also hoping to connect with people who wanted to do more than talk. I wanted us to create something meaningful that respected nature, ourselves, and each other. I wanted to have an open dialogue and not sit for endless hours listening to people telling me how to be and "create my own reality." They didn't know me and yet pretended like they knew what was best for me.

In an attempt to support a friend, I found myself at the last workshop I will ever attend where there is a "teacher" with a manual instructing me (without knowing anything about me) on how to manifest using her proven five steps. I am wary of being instructed on how to be curious, manifest, and be present. The bullshit meter was running in my mind as a binder I was to follow was thrust into my hands. How can you manifest in a world where the cultural, economic, and political frameworks that shape how we live are broken and falling apart? If you wish or dream it, will it automatically reflect your peace and harmony? Could I not feel how beautifully the instructor was shifting the energy in the room with what she told us was her unique "big energy"? Is it not delusional to believe that the world will simply transform when we get together and manifest together? Doesn't it take creation and investment to birth something into the world? And my heart was cautioning me that there's a cost to everything—it's worth considering why we experience these situations and what we're meant to learn.

At the edges, I met people who were as confused as I was about what was truly going on. I continued to go undercover to see what people were made of—was it simply talk or were they living and creating in a healthy way? And under the covers, I caught a glimpse of whether their actions matched their words. There were so many times I questioned myself to the core, but I could not argue with how people were simply acting and not being true to their words or philosophies. Like all of us, some had challenging relationships with their kids, siblings, or parents. And sometimes with themselves. Spending time with them, I saw that they had their own work to do. I wasn't looking to be fixed or saved by someone else or be at a higher level of consciousness; I wanted to cocreate with people who knew in their hearts that there is another way out of the crazy world we inherited.

FINDING HARMONY IN A CRAZY WORLD

Mindfulness, meditation, and yoga are beautiful practices in their purest form. I learned firsthand from Suresh Ayurveda, an amazing Ayurvedic practitioner in Ubud, Bali, that a world surrounded by stress, pressure, and outer aggression causes illness and imbalance in the body and mind. When we can see the human as a whole, not only treating physical pains but also touching the mind and soul, we can promote and accelerate our self-healing process. A return to nature also helps us get our mind back into balance and be at peace within our own heart.

Suresh opened my heart to what it means to treat the human being as a whole, connecting the physical and psychological aspects and healing both with traditional therapies and practices (not chemicals) such as Ayurveda, yoga, meditation, pranayama, reflexology, Balinese and Thai massage, craniosacral therapy, and Reiki. It was a whole new world that opened up to me. My orthopedic doctor back in San Francisco had told me to learn to live with the pain of a rib injury, and yet I knew in my heart that there was another way. Suresh recognized that I was a free spirit who struggled with structure and rules. I was elated when he introduced me to water meditation, a new form of healing that worked for me. After we worked together on getting my body aligned, I started to discover that there was an alternative way and there was no need to learn to live with the pain.

It was serendipity that, back in San Francisco, after firing myself from my corporate job, I met Karuna Patel. From the minute I met her, I loved her energy and enthusiasm. I later learned that she was a physical therapist shaking up our world to bring holistic health everywhere she went. The best way to describe Karuna is as a fierce force of nature who is a true visionary. She combines physical therapy and physical awareness to heal us holistically. She facilitates unlocking the body's natural power to heal and enhancing its magnificent performance, resulting in breakthrough recovery.

Though Karuna has been a physical therapist for more than twenty-three years, she continues to explore the unknown when it comes to healing the body, mind, and soul. Recently, a client came to her with a broken bone and torn ligaments in her foot. The first physician this client saw had told her that surgery was her only option. Because she didn't want to have surgery, she went to see another specialist, who told her that she didn't really need surgery, just some physical therapy.

Karuna didn't realize who this woman was (a celebrity to many) and asked her to share her story, not just talk about her physical pain. After listening to her story, it became apparent to Karuna that her client needed to heal on the inside, to show up more authentically in her life. As the woman began working on healing her ankle and foot, they started exploring emotional energy flow (we are more than just bones and muscles), and they both learned that changes made in her business life were creating great stress and disharmony in her life.

Karuna's holistic healing approach asks us why we would not use everything available to us to heal ourselves. Why is it so hard for so many of us to work from the inside out to create a healthy life, by no longer masking what's holding us back or causing us pain? Karuna is convinced that anyone who walks into her clinic can learn to be more authentic by feeling more at ease in their skin, understanding who they are, and expressing that and showing up that way in life. Her therapies, like these books, are for anyone who wants to explore all of life's options.

Learning how to address our limiting beliefs and conditioning can help us tremendously to get more in touch with ourselves and understand what's ours and what has been programmed into us. When I was invited to speak on a panel at a conscious leadership summit in Aspen, Colorado, I met amazing people like Flicka Rahn and Tammy McCrary, who are truly creating something meaningful in the world. Flicka is an internationally-known vocalist, composer, and sound healer with a career in academia, and Tammy is an entertainment business executive and entrepreneur who established a community for artists at artistology.com. Tammy excels in reimagining what it means to be a music industry pioneer. They are both passionate proponents of collaboration and cocreated the Innergy Tuner app, which helps to elevate and balance our emotional and energetic states.

Their music and sound healing are created at A=432 Hz. This is known as "Verdi's A," an alternative tuning frequency that is mathematically consistent with the universe. Music based on 432 Hz transmits beneficial healing energy, because it is a pure tone fundamental to nature and it allows sound to be received in a naturally harmonious, impactful, and coherent way. Flicka and Tammy share their wisdom in their groundbreaking book *The Transformational*

Power of Sound and Music and in Flicka's and Daniel Wyman's healing music for the heart. Their *Icaros: Chakra Soundscapes* (theicaros.com) helped me get grounded and is some of the best vibrational medicine for my soul.

When Flicka, Tammy, and Daniel were working with Doctors Who Rock, the doctors shared that they were simply transported by experiencing the music. The doctors felt that the sound healing helped them see fractals, sacred geometry, jewel colors, and other dimensions. It created a sonic cradle of peace, which can only be achieved with live music carrying the uncompressed harmonics that flow through Daniel's music and Flicka's voice. All of this is organic and natural, and when tuned to A=432 Hz, is easily accepted and integrated into the physical body. The true healing took place with music as medicine for the soul.

Their body of work resonated with me because I had learned from Eduardo Marturet, the maestro and music director of the Miami Symphony Orchestra, that when observing nature, you find that the Golden Ratio, derived from the Fibonacci sequence, is everywhere and appears in the foundation of art, beauty, and life—even in your DNA. Eduardo shared with me that when a child with disabilities listens to his album *@Zaha's Place*, they not only immediately connect with the music subconsciously, but their overall well-being improves. Music is a powerful unifying tool, and there are incredible people building pathways to bring our hearts and minds together in harmony. So, I learned that while I needed to be mindful of people's agendas and motivations, I could be discerning between those who could add to my life and those whose interest lies in lining their pockets or feeding their ego.

EXPERIENCING THE NEW AGE CRAZE

I threw myself deep into this New Age world for a few years, hoping to meet kindred spirits who also wanted to create healthier business and societal systems. I thought they would be on a similar journey. I even wrote an award-winning book on conscious leadership, *Our Journey to Corporate Sanity*, which has amazing stories of transformational leaders. But I soon realized how destructive some of these self-appointed spiritual teachers, shamans, and nonprofit leaders were, and that I was meant to witness it all firsthand. It was not much different than the corporate world. I found that most people were still afraid to step out of conformity with how things are done. I found that it was much easier to introduce *new* innovative programs and gurus than to address the foundation that was cracking. One nonprofit CEO asked me to go to my company and ask for a $500,000 slush fund for emergencies. My response was disbelief. Everywhere I turned, it was always about more and more money for causes, and yet the same issues of poverty, human trafficking, and access to food and water were worsening.

It was more of the same on a different channel. I attended an event where the CEO of a large global company was presented as the poster child of the mindfulness movement. I was sitting next to one of his executives at dinner, so I asked her what it was like to work there and have all these wonderful programs. She told me that it was impossible to implement them across the company because the CEO was the only one who knew how to practice them. And despite winning awards and getting good press, it was not a great place to work. But it did very well with the business of getting more customers and being more profitable.

My hope was to meet people who not only saw the dysfunctional systems but wanted to create healthier ones. It was not about warring against the machine but a new way of life that did not divide us into battlegrounds where there were winners and losers, or even spiritual "warriors." There would be enough for all of us as we focused on opportunities and creation. I spent my youth studying cultural, political, and economic systems, and I was simply tired and bored by the debates and the never-ending divisions. I was on a quest to meet creators in the world who did not need to take center stage but felt comfortable being at the edges of society.

Instead, I met a lot of broken people who were now making money by facilitating other people through their traumas when they had yet to heal themselves. These people called themselves everything from intuitive healers to philosophers. Some had no formal training, while others held doctorate degrees and certifications. Having experienced much of the world firsthand, from slums to wars, I carried a lot of our collective pain within me and knew in my heart that our world does not need to continue on this destructive trajectory. Much of the hope I experienced was in the hearts of the youth in the slums. I was also exposed to many wealthy and "successful" people who were incredibly broken and were willing to pay large amounts of money for their healing.

There was definitely a growing market of people wanting to be saved and an abundance of saviors up for the task. When I talked with some of them about the vast human suffering on the planet, I was repeatedly told by the spiritual "teachers" to focus on my own suffering, because everyone I meet is a reflection of me and my own trauma. The woman running the workshop I took part in even instructed us that "Hitler, for example, becomes a Hitler because we as a collective of sorts agreed to participate in his story." I am quite certain that my great grandparents who trusted that Austria was a cultured nation, and millions like them who were killed in concentration camps, would have a different "enlightened" perspective than this one. These "teachers" also told me they were here to save my soul, along with a bunch of other rhetoric. Carl Jung, Ram Dass, and Jesus were quoted a lot as though they held the answers to our salvation. And somehow, I have known since I was a child that no one is coming to save us from ourselves.

I did meet some wonderful people, but what I kept experiencing was that rather than being a way to awaken people to our true nature and the roots of greed and societal success, what I experienced was a movement using the same principles of industrialized business. People have been expected to adapt and change to what the models demand of them and there is manipulation, unhealthy design, and individual gain built into the fabric of these dying systems. It is a fact more than a belief. Corporate practices and managerial decisions have conditioned us to accept unsustainable growth and greed. It is delusional to believe that practices meant to improve productivity and address stress will help you deal with the burnout of working more than eighty hours a week and being expected to be available 24/7.

There is no simple way out of the structures we have constructed, such as human trafficking, which is estimated to be a $150-billion "industry" with 66 percent of the global profits coming from sexual exploitation. The UN-backed International Labor Organization estimates that up to forty million people globally are affected by this industry. It is second only to drug trafficking as the world's largest criminal "industry." Human trafficking often involves the legitimate services of business, for example the banking system, transportation companies, the hospitality sector, health care providers, digital social media platforms, and corrupt government systems. It's happening right now and the world remains mostly silent. But our opportunity is to go to the root cause and address it, not pour more outrage on the suffering of so many. It's our time to step into our power and break these never-ending cycles, because we can—all of our children need us now more than ever.

The fact that someone is tracking the business and economics of modern-day slavery is insane. Anyone can easily access reports showing that the market rate of a young girl or boy is fourteen dollars. There is no aspirin strong enough to get us out of this reality. Many nonprofits are working endlessly to make a dent in this horrific scenario that is a reality for those caught in it, and yet it is still here now, right here in our collective world. It's always been here. But can we finally put a stop to all the fighting, divisions, and conflicts and find healthy ways to take care of ourselves and each other?

YOU CAN SIT QUIETLY AND GO INWARD AND MANIFEST, AND YOU CAN ALSO STAND UP AND SAY, "ENOUGH!"

It's easy to get seduced and mesmerized by celebrity and fame. How many people want to meet Oprah and get her autograph or have her endorse them so they too can be in front of billions of people? How did we get to being a world of influencers and celebrating one person over another? The reality is that we are the ones who elevate people like Oprah and keep this insane celebrity culture of fame alive through our actions. At the end of the day, celebrities are as human as we are. Oprah has hardships, as does everyone else on the planet to varying degrees, but we've elevated her to this special status that has become the dream of many people.

And sure, she has the power to make or break people. But how did she get it? Who gave her this special pass? And why do so many people listen to her wisdom or dream of having her read their book or endorse their product? We all know how powerful she is in the current system. One endorsement can literally change your life, as it did for Jon Kabat-Zinn, the father of modern mindfulness. Those who own the latest solutions can step in and save the day. And yet, look around at our world. What has changed, apart from the latest fad or craze? Did everyone become happy and Zen overnight? Then why is there still human trafficking? I'd love for someone to help me understand this.

The only thing I discovered was that putting lipstick on a bulldog only irritates the bulldog. It is unnatural to expect anything to shift unless we address the root cause, and also see the opportunity. The easiest thing to do is throw stones and fight. It takes another level of courage to look deeper at the environment, as well as at ourselves. It's not separate. Nature is made of holistic systems. There is merit in sitting still and focusing on what's in front of you. I have been doing a lot of internal work—it is a daily practice—but the way I am doing it may not be for you. I continue to learn what and who is for me, and what isn't, simply by showing up every day and questioning everything. I have archived other people's manuals—I'm thankful that they work for them, but I've found a capacity to do my own work.

I have met incredible individuals who are accentuating natural systems in music that have helped me become more mindful and centered. But I still ache for the suffering of so many people around me trying to make a life. How can I not feel utter sadness for the boys and girls being trafficked—right now, as you are reading or listening to this—and being sold to the highest bidder for an average of fourteen dollars? How can my heart not break into a million pieces knowing there is a way out when we do not ignore reality? How can anyone teach that this horrific external reality is simply a reflection and mirror of me and could just go away with a little "love and light"?

Author Ronald Purser, in his book *McMindfulness: How Mindfulness Became the New Capitalist Spirituality*, advises us:

"A commitment to this kind of privatized and psychologized mindfulness *is* political ... Mindfulness-based interventions fulfill this purpose by therapeutically optimizing individuals to make them 'mentally fit,' attentive and resilient, so they may keep functioning within the system. Such capitulation seems like the farthest thing from a revolution and more like a quietist surrender.

Celebrity role models bless and endorse it, while "cool" Californian companies—including Google, Facebook, Twitter, Yahoo, Salesforce, Apple, and Zynga—have embraced it as an adjunct to their brand. Google's former in-house mindfulness tsar Chade-Meng Tan had the actual job title Jolly Good Fellow. 'Search inside yourself,' he counseled colleagues (as well as readers of his bestselling book), for there—not in corporate culture—lies the source of your problems.

The rhetoric of 'self-mastery,' 'resilience' and 'happiness' assumes wellbeing is simply a matter of developing a skill. Mindfulness cheerleaders are particularly fond of this trope, saying we can train our brains to be happy, like exercising muscles. Happiness, freedom and wellbeing become the products of individual effort. Such so-called 'skills' can be developed without reliance on external factors, relationships, or social conditions. Underneath its therapeutic discourse, mindfulness subtly reframes problems as the outcomes of choices. Personal troubles are never attributed to political or socio-economic conditions but are always psychological in nature and diagnosed as pathologies. Society therefore needs therapy, not radical change. This is perhaps why mindfulness initiatives have become so attractive to government policymakers. Societal problems rooted in inequality, racism, poverty, addiction and substance abuse and deteriorating mental health can be reframed in terms of individual psychology, requiring therapeutic help. Vulnerable subjects can even be told to provide this themselves."

Sitting in silence, watching my breath and waiting, was not for me. The good life was not going to simply show up, but the healthy path started emerging as I began to discern between those selling to me and those caring for me. I learned to look deep inside of people, and, while I was conditioned to give people the benefit of the doubt, I learned how to walk away (and often run) faster, as empty promises and solutions had no space in my life. And believe me, I am not close to being done, which is why I am putting this trilogy into the world now, to let you know you are not alone. I wished someone had been there for me, and then I realized *I* was someone and I had a responsibility to create something meaningful for all of us.

I shied away from both inflated promises of manifesting and doing shadow work with people who were toxic for me—both of these let me see how lost the people are who aspire to be the new generation of spiritual teachers. But not everyone was like that. There are gems in the world who care deeply and want to imagine, dream, and create together, and they are grounded in reality. There is no magic bullet or secret that erases trauma. It takes a lot of work and guidance from truly healthy people who can support and care for you. The work entails finding your own source of power and voice so you don't need to be swayed by the status quo or the latest quick-fix program that entices you to someone else's agenda. What is the collective story that you want to create that includes your strongest desires and allows you to show up unmasked, real, and raw?

The divisions in our world run deep and are by design. Turn on your television and you will see series and movies branded as dramas, thrillers, or comedies, and they illustrate some of the reality around you. In every joke, there is a kernel of truth. The irony is that the corruption is not only playing out on our screens but in reality. Look at our history: mob mentality has been incited for years. Consensus and groupthink have become a toxic element in today's world where healthy decisions are not being made. You may have been instructed not to let your imagination run wild by people who feared what you could imagine.

Neil Postman, an author, educator, media theorist, and cultural critic, observed that "we had learned how to invent things, and the question of why we invent things receded in importance. The idea that if something could be done it should be done was born in the nineteenth century. And along with it, there developed a profound belief in all the principles through which invention succeeds: objectivity, efficiency, expertise, standardization, measurement, and progress. It also came to be believed that the engine of technological progress worked most efficiently when people are conceived of not as children of God or even as citizens but as consumers—that is to say, as markets [and audiences]."

When someone tells you "this is how things are done" or diagnoses you in a category, like being a victim, it is not an invitation to cocreate. It's about you fitting into their world where everyone fits into that culture and way of doing things. It's a huge challenge and opportunity we have in this world, because many people who think they are open are not aware that they are stuck in their story, that there is a bigger world out there where they can let go of what keeps them trapped in how things "should" be. You can sit in a quiet space on your cushion and go deep inside, but then you face the same issues at work and the same stress of paying your bills, all delivered to you daily. When you start looking at the root cause of stress, you can begin to see the opportunity and approach it holistically. You can begin to see what and who you are facing with healthier eyes.

The beliefs about right and wrong, good and bad, true and false, and appropriate and inappropriate are up to you to examine. Many of these beliefs fragment and divide us inside ourselves and from the world around us. I encourage you to discover forgiveness, find ways to act without judgment, remain openhearted, and love yourself deeply, with the kind of love and recognition you seek from others. Opening your heart allows you to observe your judgments, perspectives, and beliefs, as well as the stories you create about yourself, life, and others. When you allow yourself to connect with the truth, power, and wisdom within, you will find yourself being carried forth in a healthy direction. It takes practice to balance a steady flow of inner peace, tap into abundant resources and joyful experiences by grounding and getting centered, integrating any suppressed emotional charges that get triggered, and monitoring your vibration. Remember that when you put your fate into your own hands, you tap into your personal power and ability to work through issues and find your rhythm and balance.

How can you have more authority over your own life? Can you use your heart to source what you would like to experience and what is possible for you? The most important medicine comes from healthy soil and souls. Be discerning about what and who you allow into your life, and learn to let go of stories and people who no longer walk the path with you. The universe is asking each of us to get more real.

EXPEDITION 24

UNCOVERING THE FULL EXPRESSION OF YOUR HEART

♥

People who know how to manipulate—like marketers, advertisers, psychopathic leaders, and anyone who has a specific agenda—excel in figuring out how they can get us to do what they want. They know that we're creatures of habit and gravitate toward predictability and safety. Their mission is to identify our patterns, behaviors, and likes and to convince and sell us on why we need what they have. Recognizing and understanding your value in the equation and pinpointing what others want—a new customer and a sale, or a vote and a political win—is key information in helping you make a conscious choice about whether you want their goods or beliefs. Knowing your value makes you aware of when someone is trying to manipulate you. Universal law teaches us that if it's too good to be true, then it's often not true.

We live in a society where we are constantly compared to others. Advertisers take full advantage of this fact, using what they would have us believe beauty is: models and actors with perfect lifestyles and gorgeous bodies for us to fantasize over. They try to persuade us that if we buy their products we too can have this wonderful, desirable, perfect life. Commercials and social media influencers epitomize the current love affair so many people have with following those in the know. We allow influencers to set the latest fashion trends and the popularity of car makes and models, home and garden furnishings, beauty and wellness products, books and entertainment, and state-of-the-art technology. Advertisers target particular socioeconomic groups and use our buying habits as a way to become more and more profitable. The financial growth of corporations is driving these markets and consequently undermining our life with the belief that it will not be happy unless we stay current with the best products and services they offer.

THINGS AREN'T ALWAYS WHAT THEY SEEM

It is a game to these highly successful sales and marketing leaders, who make a lot of money from consumer spending. They are in fact competing with each other to see who can reach the sales targets first or break the record for their department and earn the biggest commission check. And then there are the psychopaths who make up 20 percent of the global "leaders" of our world. Bernie Madoff, for example, was a very well-respected stockbroker and investment adviser in the financial services industry, and the former nonexecutive chairman of the Nasdaq stock market. Madoff convinced thousands of people that he could get a 50 percent return on their investments in ninety days. It turned out that he amassed $65 billion in one of the largest Ponzi schemes in history. All he did was pay the investors with the money he received from the new investors he convinced to join his game. He later confessed to his sons that their business was "one big lie." The Madoff scandal left a long trail of wreckage that included lost homes, bankruptcies, divorces, depression, and suicides. Madoff persuaded more than ten thousand people to trust him with their investments, falsely promising consistently high returns.

Egoism and selfishness, which spread like a virus, thrive on narcissism, exploitation, and manipulation. Many sociopaths lose sight of any humanity as they get seduced by greed, power, and status. NXIVM, a multilevel marketing organization promising a path to happiness through personal development programs, is now widely described as a cult. Its self-improvement workshops seduced many successful people in Hollywood and business who were searching for a higher purpose in life. But underneath its facade, NXIVM was not only a recruiting platform for a secret society that physically branded women and forced them into sexual slavery but was also designed to feed the sick delusions of a sociopathic guru who convinced many people that he had their answers.

In 2020, Keith Raniere, NXIVM's leader, was sentenced to 120 years in prison for federal crimes, sex trafficking, and racketeering. The funding of the NXIVM machine came, in large part, from the heiress to the Seagram's liquor fortune, Clare Bronfman, who spent more than $100 million of her inheritance to fund the organization and also to sue Mr. Raniere's accusers. She was sentenced and ordered to serve six years and nine months in federal prison. Another of NXIVM's top recruiters was Allison Mack, the former television actress known for her role on *Smallville*, whose glowing testimonials helped bring Hollywood celebrities into the organization. There was repeated mention of how Jennifer Aniston, Gerard Butler, and Sir Richard Branson took NXIVM classes, even if they didn't become full-fledged members. The Dalai Lama once spoke at a NXIVM event after being assured by the Bronfman sisters that it was a legitimate organization.

In an article in *Esquire*, called "How NXIVM Seduced Hollywood Stars and America's Most Powerful Elite into a Barbaric 'Sex Cult'," Lauren Kranc writes, "Raniere was hailed as an elusive, god-like savant by his followers." She shared that for many from the outside looking in, what he had to offer seemed like the perfect life. But instead of providing a path to happiness, Raniere and his "leadership" team destroyed the lives of thousands and their families. And this is another story of a sociopath in our sick world who preyed on people who were looking for answers to the secret of a successful life and ended up having their sanity, trust, and bank accounts cleaned out.

It happens all the time at different levels, and it can happen to anyone. We have been conditioned to think that someone outside ourselves has our answers or holds our power. So many of us want to belong and be part of something bigger than ourselves. I've heard people say that they would be able to know right away if they were being recruited into a cult or someone's scheme. But often, those of us who believe we are too smart to get sucked in are enticed by promises of self-improvement and a supportive community. In fact, over two-thirds of cult members are brought in by a family member or a friend who is deemed trustworthy. When someone offers a front row seat to the secrets of the universe, anyone seeking answers can be tempted. And the seduction of being loved and cared for is what most are seeking. When you read about cults and deprogramming— which I have, for some reason, since the age of fourteen—you learn that there's a lesson in everything.

This is the reason I no longer choose to live in a hero or celebrity culture. I don't know who your heroes are, but if one of them said, "This is really great," you might be drawn to it. In 2009, the Dalai Lama accepted an invitation to speak at an event attended by three thousand NXIVM members. At one point, he placed a ceremonial Tibetan scarf, known as a *khata*, around Keith Raniere's neck. This act was a symbolic gesture of acceptance. Now, if the Dalai Lama endorses the leader of NXIVM, and all these celebrities think he's great, it's much harder to question this belief, is it not?

Psychopathic traits often include a lack of remorse and empathy, a sense of grandiosity, superficial charm, manipulative behavior, and refusal to take responsibility for one's actions. For politicians, possessing excessive charm and a calculating mind is considered an asset. Research has found that there are at least three times as many psychopaths in executive or CEO roles than in the overall population. But recent data by forensic psychologist Nathan Brooks shows that it's now a much higher figure.

And remember that it is we and our ancestors who have allowed our countries and organizations to be led by these sociopathic "leaders." Anyone who has been in an abusive relationship has come into contact with an insidious liar and their trickster energy— someone pretending to be the exact opposite of their truth. Once you can clearly see the manipulation and deceit that is happening, you can start addressing the wounds and going to the root cause of your seduction. It takes a lot of compassion, self-reflection, and curiosity to heal ourselves.

Inner work involves healthy doses of undoing and unraveling. As we discussed in *F*ck the Bucket List for the Adventurer*, flow is key as we tap into the intelligence of nature. We can choose to fight the wave and let it hit us with thousands of ripples of pain, or we can teach ourselves to ride the wave by trusting the currents. Each one of us has screwed up along the way and trusted people who were toxic to our well-being. It doesn't mean that we must stay in our own prison when the opportunity is to learn and grow at our own pace.

The best revenge is no revenge; the best revenge is living well by learning to understand that our energy and attention are our most valuable assets, and how we invest and use them is up to us. It takes forgiveness of ourselves and courage to find our own path in our own way. Otherwise, we simply relive our history over and over with reruns and sequels of the same story.

WE CAN'T DRAG THE PAST EVERYWHERE WE GO

There is no need to harm ourselves or anyone else when we become conscious, healthy creators. There is a fine line between intentionally manipulating others for personal gain and making mistakes, failing, and learning from them. Part of personal growth comes from becoming aware of people's intentions and understanding the role you play in their game, especially when they see you as the target demographic for their marketing goals or political scheme. And becoming aware of whether their intentions are pure and healthy for you is key, because they don't really care what happens to you once you buy into their plan. It is just as easy or hard to set boundaries and walk away from someone's scheme as it is to get swept in and fall in love with their "promise."

We have learned to fall in love with our problems, and when we really think about it, many of them are self-created. Since all of us tend to be predictable to some extent, we should be aware of our habits and behaviors and where our actions and reactions are predictable. Have you ever been caught in someone else's scheme? Have you noticed anyone around you who has the ability to manipulate others? Learning how to read the signs and becoming aware of how you react will help you avoid getting dragged into someone else's ruse. Discover their end goal and what is feeding their ego. Be brave enough to ask direct questions. This is where listening is important, not just to their words but to how your body and gut reacts with your inner knowing and compass. Take note of their answers and whether they are consistent over time.

Being constantly pushed for an answer or commitment is a red flag. Unless it's a life-or-death situation, then it is possible to negotiate more time. The healthiest reaction is often to be silent and listen; I often simply say nothing when someone tries to pressure me or seduce me into taking sides. It is amazing to observe how people react when you don't comment or chime in—they continue talking to fill the void of silence. As they talk, they reveal more about what they want, how they are going to get it, and what they are going to do. The more you listen, the more you will hear and obtain a clearer picture as to what is going on and whether they are able to walk their talk.

As you practice setting boundaries and having clarity about what and who is for you and not for you, you will more quickly be able to identify those who are healthy for you and those who are not. And it is your journey to take to find out. Remember, you will keep attracting similar situations or people until you can see the pattern and learn who is truly healthy for you. Setting boundaries is a way to take care of yourself. Just because you don't do things the way someone else wants you to, doesn't mean that you are selfish or uncaring. It simply means that you also matter and know how to take care of yourself. While you may have been conditioned to not disappoint others, setting boundaries allows you to love yourself, so then you can love others, when you are ready. You can be kind to someone else when you begin by being kind to yourself. On the other hand, if you are facing a negotiation like a divorce or a house sale where all sides need to be right, a knee-jerk reaction can set off a chain of events that leads to deadlock and misunderstandings.

The key is to listen and determine what the other party's goal is and whether you want to find the healthy conclusion for all or walk away and find something better for your needs. This journey is one of letting go, and where we're headed there's no need for senseless competition, judgment, greed, hate, violence, control, or manipulation. It's up to you to closely examine all your beliefs and patterns and let go of the ones that no longer suit you.

View each challenge as an opportunity to cocreate a healthy environment for yourself and your community. There's no reason to do any harm to yourself, anyone else, or anything. Ask yourself, in what areas am I in balance and where am I experiencing disharmony and discomfort? It's an opportunity to discover personal methods of grounding to maintain your balance. Identify the actions, thoughts, people, and situations in your life that support you in feeling anchored to Grandmother Earth and the truth of your heart. As you establish a sense of groundedness and balance, you create clarity and peace within your being.

HOW DID WE GET TO A PLACE WHERE SO MANY PEOPLE WANT TO BE RIGHT ALL THE TIME?

Imagine a system conceived to help you understand who you are as an individual and provide metrics on how you are growing and improving, compared to none other than yourself. Instead, you are taught to compete with others in order to succeed, sending the subliminal message that someone else must lose. Our infrastructures to date have all been constructed on win-lose models. For someone to win, someone else must lose, and so the story goes. Do you have a need to always be right? Why? What's so great about being right? Where does this need or desire come from? Are you surrounded by others who have to be right all the time? Do you know where their need stems from? What does being right actually mean to you?

The need to win is deeply rooted in each of us as a result of our upbringing or conditioning. Did you have to win your parents' approval or strive for their affection and love? Did you have to compete with a sibling who got to do the easiest chores or was given candy or an extra cookie for doing well? When you can remember where and when these practices began, you can begin to understand what is driving you to do the things you do, and whether they are beneficial or detrimental to your well-being. Maybe you were led to believe that children should be seen and not heard, which is tantamount to being shut down to keep yourself small and in the shadow of others.

At school, you might have been humiliated by always being the last one picked for the team and feeling you were everyone's last choice. You might have figured that having the loudest voice or acting out would put you in the spotlight, or that having a temper tantrum would eventually get you your own way, or that shutting others down would give you the attention you never got at home.

We become accustomed from a very young age to what is acceptable and unacceptable behavior. To survive, we had to play by the rules, because of course we relied on parents or grown-ups to provide necessities such as shelter, food, and clothing. This training is compounded as we grow up and apply it to our conditioning in adulthood, but it doesn't mean that we have to continue that way. It is necessary to pause and question our conditioning and to release the areas that are no longer serving us. Can you imagine the possibilities if every kid felt inspired, not compelled, to be their best?

When you can open up to the possibility that you may be wrong, that's when the magic happens. It allows you to see a different perspective and perceive the beauty in truth without blaming anyone outside of yourself. You may have learned to tread carefully because there are so many different points of view, and there is a danger— you can open yourself up to criticism and judgment if you speak your truth. This is not just the truth, it's the healthier thing to do for yourself. This is imperative when truly honoring and respecting yourself and your thoughts and feelings. Maybe it's time to consider that winning at all costs may no longer serve you, as the cost of losing is getting to be too high.

We have been hardwired to win and be right. Winning and being right indicates that you are the best and smartest. You earn a top score for being right and are deemed better than anyone else. Great sports champions share their winnings and successes with their team and those that helped them along the way. Otherwise, it can be very lonely at the top, sitting there all by yourself with your trophy and bag of money, separated from everyone else. Where's the joy in being a winner and being right? How long does the high last before you look around and realize maybe "the win" isn't so great after all?

What happens when you can identify your programming and upgrade your operating system? What if you can learn how to not take yourself so seriously and understand that healthy competition helps you grow but crushing others really does not serve anything apart from your ego?

In heated conversations, when people are competing with each other instead of communicating, try to throw a joke into the mix to lighten the energy and break the tension. As the old Arab proverb says, "When you shoot an arrow of truth, dip its point in honey."

In the adult playground, one easy way to take the wind out of their sails is to agree with the person who needs to be right. You can also admit that you are wrong and watch how they react. If you want to continue a relationship, it takes nothing away from you to let them feel they've "won" an argument. You might later find that the opportunity presents itself where they realize their attachment to being right and the whole incident allowed everyone to learn and grow!

Until you understand that there is beauty in cocreation around a shared purpose of what you want to create in your life, you will continue to remain locked in the unconscious program of dominating one another. The silly beliefs you hold keep you deadlocked in the drama of right or wrong, good or bad, appropriate or inappropriate. In this reality, you find yourself offended or blaming some external force for the injustice of it all.

When you base your self-worth on being right about everything, you get attached to how the world "should" be and prevent yourself from learning and growing. You fear seeing something in a different light and close yourself off from what is possible. It's healthy to assume that you don't have all the answers because it keeps you unattached to being right and helps you with your mission on Earth to learn and grow by trial and error. And one of the things you may learn is that creation involves more than just material, tangible things. Having healthy conversations where you listen to each other and learn is an act of creation as well. When you have a heated disagreement, feel the energy and how you are creating battle lines and conflict. And then feel the energy when you are having healthy dialogue. In which reality do you want to live?

On a recent trip, the ridesharing driver got into a deep conversation with me and started asking me a lot of questions when I told him I was an author. I told him that because I did not know him, I could not offer him advice but could listen and ask him questions. When I got to my destination and was about to step out of his car, he wanted to talk about one more thing. He turned to me and shared that he was having problems with his wife—they were arguing all the time, and he needed to be right because it was culturally known that he was the man of the house. When he was done sharing, I asked him, "Why did you marry her?" He looked at me, puzzled, and said, "Because I love her." I said, "Exactly. So, do you want to come home every night and have an argument and go to bed hurt, or have love in your life? What's the cost of being right to you and the person you love?"

Is it not time to take a step back and question how we got here? It will require a closer look at situations and being truthful with ourselves about what we want to get out of them. So, you won, now what? Was it worth the struggle? What does being right provide you with? What does it cost you? How can you shift, if that is what you choose to do? Is there someone around you who can give you feedback and thoughts that could help you, or do you need to spend time on your own reflecting on your own belief system?

We've been taught that sensitivity and emotions are the enemy of success. How did we get to a place where we're so jaded that our humanity is buried deeply under insensitivity and ruthless ambition? How did we get to a place where our core foundation is based on survival? Why not imagine a healthy and different mindset that includes everyone, with compassion for their needs?

LET THE WORLD FEEL YOUR HEARTBEAT

"Let the world feel your heartbeat" are the words my dear friend Tim McDonald lives by, and a tattoo he has on his arm. Tim guides us to follow our hearts and intuition through his talks, workshops, and writing. Tim believes that we may never know the impact that the ripples we make today are going to have on people, but we just need to trust that it's so. We need to understand that we will affect some people and never hear about it. We need to know that our actions will create an impact in the world, even though we might not be able to tangibly put our finger on it or set our eyes on it to see that it happened. "Being good to people," Tim shares, "doesn't take a world-changing event. It can be as simple as a smile, opening the door, or just listening to someone who needs to know they are not alone."

Tim is a visionary who walks his talk. He is a true creator in our world and is passionate about connecting people with purpose. It's been said that Tim is ahead of his time. In his high school years, he yearned to be a free spirit. He built a community for community managers before most people had even heard of the term. This led to his being a pioneer in establishing community management at The Huffington Post. Tim experiences life on the edges, connecting deeply with people and building long-term, purposeful relationships. He brings many lessons to his creations in the world that he openly speaks and writes about. By dealing with weighty issues, he has found meaning and is doing his life's work.

When he was diagnosed with stage IV cancer during the middle of the pandemic, his work took an even more meaningful turn. He wrote, spoke, and brought people together like never before. His rawness and openness inspired many of us to see the seeds he planted throughout his life come into full bloom. So many people have responded and openly shared with Tim how he has touched their lives, and it has been incredible to witness the ripples of his generous heartbeat. He has also encouraged everyone to get a colonoscopy and has provided information about becoming more health conscious through clean eating and alternative therapies.

Tim's outlook is infectious, in the healthiest way possible. He openly talks about fear and shares that "Having stage IV colon cancer helped me see what's possible. How I used fear in a way to have a healthy mindset that led to a significant reduction in my cancer in three months. I've taken years of conditioning and unlearned it by looking deep inside myself to live life on my terms for most of the last six years. I've gone from going through the motions to seeing everything as an adventure again."

Just by being who he is, Tim guides us to something that every human being yearns for—just to belong to something greater than ourselves. That is the essence of community. When you can provide that sense of belonging to somebody, you're filling a need for them, and you're getting something in return because they will invest in what you're doing. And together, you will create something that's greater than either of you could have made on your own. No manipulation or gurus required. Just pure love.

Tim joins us here in asking you, what is something that has happened in your life that you haven't given yourself enough credit for? What are the things you enjoy doing the most, even if they aren't making you money? Now, step back and look at what they may mean and how you can get started in a new direction. Only you know what is healthy for you. Trust yourself to start on your path. Focus on the journey and not the destination.

THERE IS VALUE IN EVERYTHING, AND SOMETIMES IT'S A BROKEN HEART

There is a silent, growing awareness of our power as individuals. Until now, we may not have been aware of the power we have to destroy our habitat and that we also have the power to prevent the destruction of the environment. As our awareness of that power grows, we become more conscious of the value of being conscientious and mindful, and we can see the impact of this awareness in many areas. More than government, more than nationality, more than religion, imagining and then living a healthy life is the most potent social organizer in the world. Because when we can imagine life, we will reimagine government and how power is distributed in the world. When we think about what means we can use to create a healthier world, conscious business comes to mind as a very obvious and powerful tool. And a great deal depends on whether we give it our power or tap into our ability to shape our collective future.

Humanity is being called to grow up, take on its fears, and exercise responsibility. This can be an anxiety-producing transition for individuals, and it is a powerful anxiety-producing transition for humanity as a whole, as social responsibility becomes very personal and ties us all to the outcome of our collective actions. It's no longer something that someone else must do.

There are pioneers, like Bryan Welch, publisher and author of *Beautiful and Abundant: Building the World We Want.* Bryan believes that business has been crafted as a vehicle for the ego. We motivate businesspeople and customers through various kinds of appeals to the ego. That is the traditional route of business. There is a general feeling that it is the only way to motivate people. But, in his experience as a farmer, the practice of farming continuously lowers one's estimation of one's own ego, because one is facing life and death every day. Many times a day, one life form or another is dying on Bryan's farm, making him much more aware of death than if he didn't farm, and driving home the knowledge that we will die as well. The constant awareness of looming mortality makes him feel that the fruits of his labor are more important for their long-term consequences than for how much money they can generate or whether he can get his name on a building at his alma mater. It strikes him as very wrong to deny his own mortality or not to plan for it every day.

Success on Bryan's farm is achieved by encouraging health in a very holistic way, concentrating first and foremost on the health of the soil and watching every day for things that are out of balance, and then trying to bring them back into balance without exerting so much force that they throw them out of balance in the other direction. That's how he defines holistic management. Bryan always loved the old saying that the best fertilizer for any property is the footprint of its owner or steward.

Bryan has sensed over the years that where they really succeeded on the farm was in their focus on the fundamental health of the environment. They have not exploited the land. They let the land and the animals operate, flourish, and reproduce based on their natural design. Some of their projects will take longer than a human life span. If you are going to do it in a holistic way and respect the wholeness and encourage real health, you have to be willing to operate on time frames that are longer than a career or a human life. You just have to trust that it's the healthy thing to do and derive satisfaction from knowing that it is the best choice for the land. The awareness of mortality that is fostered through their experience of farming helps them think on that long-term scale of several lifetimes, because they watch hundreds of lifetimes pass every year.

Bryan has learned interesting lessons from looking at the differences between farming on his property and farming on the property that is a quarter-mile east of his house and the property that is a quarter-mile west. The soils are different, the topography is different, and the hydrology is different. They would have to adopt a whole new plan—different animals, different numbers, different methods—if they were sitting even one quarter-mile away. He finds this to be a very important lesson for business. As we institutionalize business knowledge, we like to think that we can apply universal rules to what defines success in business or how you run a business and that there are best practices that can be easily applied across the board. If you run a business in a holistic and mindful way, there are countless variations. Customers, climates, and technology vary from place to place.

What if the purpose of our lives in this century is to provide value for society? This is a turning point where we're starting to shift our views of how we live, including changing our relationship with employment. The beauty of creation is that if you see life as a grand adventure, you become a creator instead of simply a doer following someone else's manual. In this transformation, where does your power lie? How can you work with a higher purpose? What is the full expression of your heart?

In an article called "The Value of a Broken Heart," Bryan openly shares the story of how he lost his son Noah, who at twenty-six chose to leave the planet. As a person who suddenly lost someone very close to me when I was twenty-six, I cried as I read the words that sprung off my computer screen and into my heart. Bryan beautifully writes:

> "Grief can be like the ocean. Its surface is turbulent. Waves tumble us about. We struggle to catch a breath before we're submerged again, then we're inverted ten feet down, the pressure excruciating. Then, inexplicably, a flash of light and a breath of air at the surface again. Deep grief can be like the deep ocean. In the midnight zone, too deep for sunlight to penetrate, there's no sign of the storm on the surface. It's cold and dark. It can be very still. Not much is living there. One can feel the slightest current from something—or someone— swimming near in the darkness.
>
> In my abyss I felt newly connected to the suffering in the world. My own sadness was strong, so pervasive, so much a part of my moment-to-moment awareness that it didn't feel practical or necessary to protect myself from the suffering of others anymore. I couldn't disguise or anesthetize my vulnerability. I cried, uncontrollably, in front of the television at home. I cried in business meetings. I cried in restaurants. I cried on airplanes... My broken heart was damaged, for sure, but it was also more open than it had been. I grew more interested in the sadness and pain of other people, pain I realized I had been blocking all my life."

Every one of us has our own story. There is an opportunity to rekindle the art of conversation and learn to truly listen to yourself, and then to others. Too often, when you are having a conversation with someone, they will interrupt you midsentence and ask if you have read this or that latest book, or if you are using this or that latest app, and so on. By just articulating a few words, they have tried to connect you to something that is familiar to them. Their intent is usually one of wanting to be helpful, and though the book or app they mention may be valuable to you, their comment shows that they are not actively listening. Most of us have been conditioned to focus on being smart and knowledgeable, but the opportunity is there to be compassionate and empathetic as well. A lot happens when we start listening more fully.

The best-selling brand in our world today is fear. It gets fake ratings, likes, and followers. It wins hearts and minds. It generates clicks. It spreads like wildfire. Most of our current social media networks continue to be built on archaic advertising and subscription models. Most are still offered for "free" in exchange for massive amounts of personal information. They have introduced old-world practices, such as "likes," that can actually inhibit or discourage people from connecting at a deeper level. The so-called "influencers" and "experts" are usually more concerned with marketing strategies than making a genuine impact. Keep in mind that if the product you are using on the internet is free, you and your actions are likely the real product, and your behavioral information is being sold to others.

True social networks, like the one introduced in the *Epilogue* of this book, will provide us with opportunities to connect more deeply in conversation, as they will have no "likes" or "followers." It's up to you to choose how to integrate these tools into your life and follow your own intuition rather than some prescribed formula for "success." It's never about the technology but rather the value we attribute to it. Step back and look closer at who holds your power.

What questions are you asking? What if you chose to see opportunity instead of only problems? What if you started every interaction focused on the opportunities first? What would your stories and our world look like then?

Why do so many of us choose to live within our comfort zones, remaining stuck in behaving like everyone else, merely playing it safe and surviving, instead of living life more passionately and thriving? What happens when you start realizing that the world as you know it is changing faster than you ever imagined, and instead of seeking comfort or safety, you start seeing safety itself as being potentially too risky? You often hear about the 1 percent as the people holding all the power and wealth in our world today. I want to introduce you to another percentage: the population that is exploring possibilities and opportunities on the edges, outside the mainstream. This population understands that the bell curve and sameness in life are no longer helpful. They see opportunities in creating a full life by connecting with people across the world or in local communities.

Change happens every time your expectations are disrupted, which means every time something makes you uncomfortable; then there is an opportunity for change. The change that is here and available to each of us is a mindset shift. We don't need to wait for it to come from the boss or the leader of the organization; it can come from you. One of the biggest shifts happening in our world today is that many people are waking up to the fact that life is precious and that they have more meaningful choices than they have believed possible. It's happening every day, often quietly, especially with people who are questioning the judgment system that society has instilled in them.

Life has taught me to set my own course and question established conventions rather than arbitrarily accept them. When you don't have the "right" ticket to get in the door, you can imagine other pathways or stay trapped when you choose to conform. I have found ways, without having the correct ticket, to get the gatekeeper to allow me in. Or I simply take the road less traveled and never look back. There is always a way through to the truth, and it takes curiosity and playfulness.

You can become addicted to safety, routine, and what you have been led to believe to be security. The known and the familiar give you predictability, but there is an associated cost. The past is known, but what's ahead today and tomorrow is not. It is to be experienced, not rehearsed. You don't need to constantly live for the future and lead a life of success. You can move into the mysterious unknown and take some risks—otherwise you become a victim of the past.

Basing your decisions and actions on logical analysis or following practical guidelines isn't quite what the universe has in mind. One way to become aware of whether you are making healthy choices is to notice your flow of energy. If saying yes to something gives you a lift of energy and makes you feel whole, then clearly that is the way forward. Conversely, if you get a negative feeling or feel resistance— your energy drops or contracts—your heart may be telling you to be careful. Trust your heart and check in with yourself.

You have a wealth of information to understand and claim from your own heart. All you are being asked to do is listen and question. Unlike lava, which spurts from a volcano and never holds back its pure eruptions, we have been trained to keep our feelings, thoughts, and desires inside ourselves. Do you feel a need to hold back what your heart is whispering to you, even in the darkest shadows? The cracks we are witnessing in the world are like cracks in the hardened arteries of the human heart. Can you feel the fracturing of the world and the unmasking of who you truly are at the heart of it all?

EXPEDITION 25

EXPLORING POSSIBILITIES

♥

sn't it funny how much energy it takes to find something that you misplaced, whether it's a pen, your keys, or your glasses. You start looking from room to room, trying to recall when you last had them or where you last used them. When you need something physical, you search and search until you find it. But when it comes to following your heart and tapping into your imagination, too often you may be afraid to search, although what's calling you is much more compelling. So many of us rely on secure places to store our most precious possessions, like jewels and documents. Yet we don't always use the same care for the most important aspect of our lives—ourselves.

We are taught to cherish the material world and fear whether our possessions are secure. We are conditioned to respect and take care of what is physical and real more than our own well-being. Many of us have learned to consume medications like painkillers; we're led to believe that there's a pill for whatever ails us and that it will provide immediate relief. And often, we do experience quantifiable and immediate results, as a headache disappears after we pop a pill.

Over a period of time, we form the belief that every time we get a headache we can ingest a pill to make the pain go away. Today, society has a pill or medicine for almost anything (with a million side effects). However, do we ever stop and think that maybe we're simply dehydrated, and the headache is trying to tell us that we need to drink more water and nurture our body? Did you know that some people drink water and eat unprocessed (raw) almonds or apples to relieve their headaches? Why don't we hear about taking care of our immune system as much as we hear about being good law-abiding citizens? Why don't we learn more about the energy of money, rather than fearing we will never have enough to live a successful life?

When we need to drive or navigate our inner self from place to place, we often get lost or overwhelmed. Taking impeccable care of ourselves can be hard work. And yet, this is when we can become aware of what's natural and unnatural in our lives. There's a deep knowledge inside of us waiting for us to listen. It takes practice, but we can develop the ability to make practical decisions for ourselves. Tapping into the invisible to form practical and material solutions takes practice, acumen, and self-awareness.

THE ILLUSION OF PERFECTION

The Japanese have a special relationship with beauty. For them, things are neither complete nor perfect. The culture, in general, pursues perfection and is very precise in business and social etiquette. But in art, they admire a certain lack of perfection. Known as *wabi-sabi* (侘寂), an imperfection is seen as an aesthetic, described as one of beauty that is imperfect, impermanent, and incomplete. The reasoning is that nothing lasts. Nothing is finished. Nothing is perfect.

Have we simply been hypnotized to believe that the way to get love and meaning in life is through our success, physical beauty, and how we appear? As a child, did we learn that chasing perfection was the goal? How could anyone expect parents who carry their own wounds and trauma—and who were taught to pursue superficial success at all costs—to guide children to a healthy life? When can we stop pursuing approval or love through perfect looks or perfect behavior and let real, raw, authentic beauty shine through? Is it when we get in touch with our tenderness and our pain that we can let go of the illusion of perfection?

Being positive all the time is not salvation; it is a misguided form of prefabricated perfection. It is by not holding back our pain, sadness, or grief that our true beauty and joy can be liberated from our minds and hearts. It is through the appreciation of being human, with all the imperfections that come with it, that love is naturally experienced. There is no need to struggle to be perfectly beautiful and attract the "right" people and circumstances into our life. Is it not enough to be aware of our gifts and curious about what we want to experiment with and experience? So, what are you attracting into your life, and what would you like to attract simply by being yourself? What's your relationship with perfection and beauty? How close are you to understanding your own *wabi-sabi* (侘 寂)?

Perfection is a state we are taught to aspire to, but it is not very realistic or plausible. When we strive for perfection, we quickly get caught in our hamster wheel again. Many New Age gurus will tell you that you are perfect as you are. Perfection is a man-made illusion. Another definition of perfection is wholeness, and wholeness is more attainable. It means the ability to naturally integrate pieces of ourselves to function harmoniously in any given situation or circumstance. Universal law teaches us that wholeness heals and that fragmentation weakens. What are the parts that keep you separate and divided within yourself, and how can you make yourself feel whole?

Most of us have brilliant ideas, but making them real takes self-knowledge, perseverance, and dedication. And I don't mean building a perfect business and selling it for millions or billions of dollars. We have very few examples of people staying true to their core, because in our world the heroes who make it in someone else's game are the ones celebrated. Perfect business growth makes up the headlines of news reports, which mostly focus on entertainment, business, and sports. If you were an alien who had just landed on our planet, you would quickly learn (and maybe question) the importance of being perfect in every aspect of life. What's your relationship with being perfect? Is it healthy or toxic to your well-being?

Most people are good at either coming up with great ideas or having the know-how to bring their ideas to fruition and work with others. We rarely have the skills to do both, which is why it's so powerful when we can create together. It is the old conflict of art versus commerce. And, yet this is the perfection we've been encouraged to strive for. Some of us were conditioned to feel that if we could only tap into our so-called superpowers, we could do it all. But we are now asking questions and wondering why we were taught that being superwoman, for example, is healthy. Many of us don't believe in the power of superheroes and want to get real when it comes to how much we take on.

It is necessary to stay grounded in reality and respect the parameters of "the game." What do I mean by this? At the end of the day, no matter how much time we spend imagining it, we cannot flap our arms and fly. No matter how much people tell you that you create your own reality or that time doesn't exist, those same people will not pick up a brick and hit their head with it, since in physical reality they will surely feel pain and possibly bleed. You can fantasize about what you want, but you have to be realistic about your energy flow and whether you can bring your vision to life with those who want to build and create with you. But as we've explored in these books, how you do it is up to you, and everything can shift in a heartbeat when you see it as your biggest opportunity.

You can strive for perfection, but make sure you don't turn whatever you're creating—whether it's a relationship, a healthier body, a new business, even a garden—into an unachievable ideal. Reflect on the purpose of your creation—who it will benefit and the impact it will have on your life or society. When creating with your imagination, balance your thoughts between perfection and practicality. In other words, if you put too much energy into being perfect, it can often kill your imagination.

INNER VISION IS THE BIRTH OF CREATION

As a child, were you filled with colorful imagination? Where did it take you and what did you imagine you could do? When was it that you started feeling a bit trapped by the many challenges of daily life? Are you still as creative as you were as a child? Are you truly able to express your creative genius to the world? You might think you never had it, but in fact you may have simply forgotten to bring your childlike imagination with you on your journey.

The process of growing up needs a reboot, as it prepares each of us to become responsible adults able to secure jobs, provide for ourselves and our families, and take care of bills. Have you ever asked yourself at what point authority figures like parents, teachers, or community leaders increasingly told you not to waste time with your silly imagination? On the other hand, you may have been rewarded for getting good grades, doing your homework, cleaning your room, having the right friends, or getting picked for the most popular sports team. And if the grown-ups told you when you were a child that your friends were not real because they couldn't see them like you could, how ashamed did it make you feel? Did you keep your imaginary friends and visions to yourself out of fear of being humiliated?

As you grew up, someone close to you probably shared their secrets to being a successful adult. Children get domesticated by caregivers about which behaviors are appropriate and which are not. It can be very confusing; we are taught to always tell the truth, but sometimes that can get us into trouble. Imagine that one day a family goes out to lunch at a busy food court. The daughter, who is seven years old, points to a woman and says in a very loud voice, "That woman has a moustache." Everyone around them is mortified and her parents feel a wave of humiliation. The little girl has unknowingly shamed her family by stating a fact, and in that one moment in time, she learns that it's inappropriate to speak freely if it hurts someone else. This is how children learn about telling the truth and start to fear what to say and how the other person is going to perceive it. Telling the truth becomes murky if it can hurt, and yet losing the ability to speak freely can sometimes prevent the real answer or solution from appearing because we are afraid of how it will be received.

Eventually, we learn that to succeed in life we must constantly strive for approval. As children, we are continually graded on how well we comply and conform with the rules given to us—and this includes being judged in art classes for our ability to be creative. It initiates and perpetuates thoughts like "Am I good enough?" that can chip away at our self-esteem. The downside of this upbringing is that it teaches us to trust everyone else before ourselves. It keeps us from discovering what we really like and what sparks us. It encourages us to compete and to learn that the winner is revered and gets special treatment.

There are many of us who feel like we sold out to become someone else, to do what is expected of us. We sometimes find ourselves too busy to think, and we feel that we have no options. We have a job, a reputation, commitments, responsibilities, and we must pay the bills. The more we have, the more we seem to need. So, we choose to continue down the path we were handed. We have come too far to change the course we take every day. We've been a "good" person overall, and we've followed the path to what we were told was the good life. But deep inside, there is a whole other conversation going on! We know in our hearts that there is another piece of us that wants to emerge and explore the edges of life.

On this road, have you found yourself having to give up being you, as part of a world that tries to make you like everyone else? Are you constantly aiming to be a better version of yourself or someone you are "supposed" to be?

It sometimes takes despair to uncover what is deep inside of you. Crying is healthy. It cleanses and helps you relinquish pent-up emotions from your body. It is an opportunity to shed any negative feelings like fear, worry, and doubt. It releases the blockages that are preventing you from uncovering the truth of who you are. It is very cathartic and allows you to step back and see things from a different perspective. It makes space when you can let go of what you've been holding in. It gives you the opportunity to see things more clearly and perhaps recognize why you have been so sad or under so much stress.

Crying helps the body calm down by getting rid of toxic emotions, and it allows you to sleep so you can rest properly and heal. Sleep is one of the best remedies for sickness because it gives the body time to restore itself. Our world would look very different if rest and nap time were not practiced only when we're very young. Every emotional incident is stored in the body. Sickness comes from holding too much in your body, which can cause ailments like headaches or stomach pains. Just like your computer needs an app or software to clean up disk space, you need to clear out your "disk" to make more room to create opportunities. How do you revitalize and release the toxins in your body?

Self-love is misunderstood today. It is not narcissism. It is a deep knowing of self, of what you need and how to honor yourself. It is important to define the difference between self-love and egoistic self-absorption and conceit. When you feel like you must please everyone else, what is the cost to yourself? Or are your needs and goals causing lack and suffering for others? It is crucial to explore and determine where you stand and what adjustments you need to make.

Too often it takes despair—reaching rock bottom—before we are forced to ask ourselves these questions. Ask anyone who has gone through a major transformation about what their breaking point was. You will likely uncover a story about a heart and mind that was awakened after a major illness or accident or a significant loss.

ARE YOU READY TO WALK INTO YOUR POWER?

The world is changing fast and providing you with opportunities to become a leader of your own life. Conscious, self-aware people are emerging around the world. Some are rewriting the established code to create healthy lives, and some are creating purposeful systems to generate industries that can contribute positively to sustaining communities.

There are many amazing developments and opportunities in our chaotic world that we can see when we start controlling the volume dial on the never-ending noise streaming into our lives. We are seeing the start of conscious businesses, healthier news sources, ways to have more open dialogue, alternative education, and leaders focused on the balance between people and profit rather than a zero sum equation. We understand that social responsibility, diversity, inclusion, and community need to be integrated into the foundation of an organization for it to be truly healthy. We have stopped *giving back*, because we didn't take anything that needed returning; our responsibility is simply to *give* and create. Harmony and unity are slowly replacing division and conformity at the edges of society, where there's no need to fight each other to be the best.

Ivan Fernández Anaya was trailing behind Olympic bronze medalist Abel Mutai during a cross-country race in Burlada, Navarra, Spain in 2013. Mutai was leading comfortably until he pulled up short of the finish line, thinking the race was over because he could not read the signs in English. Instead of passing him, Anaya slowed down and told Mutai to keep running. Since Mutai didn't speak Spanish, Anaya gestured frantically at Mutai, who went on to win the race. Later, a reporter asked Anaya, "Why did you do this?" and he replied, "My dream is that one day we can have some sort of community life where we push ourselves and help each other win." The reporter pressed, "But why did you let the Kenyan win? You could have won." He replied, "But what would be the merit of my victory? What would be the honor of this medal? What would my mother think of it?"

Universal law teaches us that healthy people flow and don't need to control others or the environment. The more you fight the current system, the more you are guaranteed to lose. The more you get real with the opportunities in front of you and create, the more you evolve into a healthier existence. What if instead of being the first or the best in a crowded market where everyone craves the spotlight, you dedicated your life to becoming a healthier version of yourself?

A lot shifts when you move away from the current programming to build the bridges you need. But we are far from truly having the communities that are needed, because many communities are not based on shared purpose (emerging world) but are formed around brands or "leaders" (dying world). These brands and leaders set the rules for what is appropriate for governing the community, which—like anything else in the world—caters to the lowest common denominator of weeding out the "bad apples."

You can stay stuck in the old system and complain about the injustices of our current world, or you can step out and create. There are millions of people hanging on for dear life right now, resisting change and believing that simply changing the deck chairs on a sinking ship will bring different outcomes. In reality, no one is coming to save us. The current systems are rotting right in front of our eyes, and healthier ones can only emerge when people like you step into your power in a healthy way—not wanting to dominate or win at all costs or take anyone down. There's too much life to live with meaning and curiosity. If we continue to give our power away, we will be watching the same movie play out over and over and over. And we know how it ends.

Conscious people acknowledge the fact that we cannot continue to pollute the Earth and the environment that supports our very existence. It is not sustainable, practical, or wise. We have gone too far and now find ourselves in a state of survival. The big question, and the most important one for all of us to playfully wrestle with, is how do we ensure financial sustainability to produce more humane practices for the collective good? We can no longer prioritize profitability at the expense of poisoning and polluting the very environment that sustains all living beings on this planet. The Earth is the source of our life, not a resource to be exploited. Fortunately, there is growing awareness that it is not prudent to breathe polluted air, drink impure water, eat cancerous foods, and consume unhealthy thoughts and beliefs. It is the acceptance of harmful and false beliefs that most urgently needs our attention and energy.

It requires an awareness of how truly powerful you are in making healthy choices, and especially in your ability to reject beliefs that pollute your mind and heart so you can free yourself from someone else's story of how you should show up and live your life. It is time for a revolution in the mindset of humanity, and it begins with you! Your mind, body, and spirit are eager to dance with nature and explore healthy possibilities. This is what is whispered to me over and over: our world needs you to be fully awake to reality so you can live a life that matters to you and supports our greater collective. What's calling you when no one is looking?

THE NEXT WAVE OF EDUCATION IS CALLING US

Author Jacob Nordby writes, "Blessed are the weird people: poets, misfits, writers, mystics, painters, troubadours, for they teach us to see the world through different eyes." I would add educators and artists to this sentiment. His guidance continues, "You know that crazy heart of yours? The one with lightning crackling and moonlight shining through it. The one you've been told not to trust because it often led you off the beaten path. The one so many have misunderstood your entire life. Trust it. Feed it. Grow it. It's your greatest treasure and will point the way to your highest destiny. It is the voice of your soul."

"From the beginning, I've felt in my heart that it's time for a big shift in perspective when it comes to education," Ashley Hollern shares with us. "It is one of the most important transformations that is needed today because it's time we give youth tools to navigate healthy paths." Ashley has been teaching in the school systems— middle school, high school, and college—for seventeen years. She also teaches science, technology, engineering, and mathematics (STEM) to teachers going back to get their degree through NASA. Ashley is a mother of four. Her eldest is fifteen and her youngest is four. Teaching, and being a student herself, has allowed her to imagine what type of education she would like children to receive. And it became clear to her, early on, that she came to our planet to find others who are rethinking how we're teaching and engaging with students and to focus on what truly matters for our collective evolution.

In 2019, Ashley was asked by futurist David Houle to speak at the Sarasota Institute, a twenty-first-century think tank in Sarasota, Florida. She had begun solidifying a vision regarding the need for teacher resources that would allow public and private teachers access to much-needed materials and contacts, with the aim of elevating and guiding education toward what she believes is a purposeful and experiential future. Ashley presented a vision called Authentic Exploration Matters, identifying what teachers, parents, and students were all seeking. This was an opportunity for collaboration, connection to relevant content, and the ability to target much-needed aid in literacy, math, science, and, most importantly, social and emotional skills that are sought by colleges and the private sector. After feedback from the presentation, and after having been thrust into the online world of education due to COVID-19 in 2020, Ashley knew it was time to seek out others and make change happen.

That is how she crossed paths with Monica Douglas, who has over twenty years of experience working in the international conservation world with organizations like the United Nations Environment Programme. Here she witnessed firsthand the overlap in numerous projects that were doing similar work. Not only was there no coordinated systemic communication and collaboration, but the projects were mostly funded separately and operating in distinct silos. The funders were not asking for information about lessons learned that could be leveraged for greater impact. Monica believes we can chart a new course for education, but this will require us to pause and rethink our way forward.

Monica and Ashley envision a world where, when it comes to education, we listen to teachers and students. Instead of trying to improve the broken system of education, they both investigated the root causes and came to the conclusion—along with many others in the field—that what's being taught in our classes is no longer relevant, especially when it comes to climate change and science. After reviewing what was being taught, they continued to introduce programs that help students become increasingly aware of climate change and the role they can play in addressing it. By taking bold steps to ensure that education will be relevant to students, they are able to tap into the hearts of children of all ages.

What better way to teach students about worldwide ecological issues than by growing coral in a lab and harnessing the power of curiosity? This is what Palm Beach Day Academy teachers Ashley Hollern and Jonathan Paine, along with their eighth- and ninth-grade students, did in the fall of 2018 by launching a yearlong project to protect coral reefs. It all started when Ashley watched the award-winning Netflix documentary *Chasing Coral* and witnessed her children's enthusiasm. She hesitantly contacted one of the leads in the film, Zack Rago, to learn more and was pleasantly surprised when he responded and agreed to talk to the students.

Children growing up in Palm Beach, Florida spend a great deal of time at the ocean. But the ones in Ashley's and Jonathan's classes never understood how much of a global problem the coral reef issue was until they started learning about it at school. A grant from the Annette Urso Rickel Foundation facilitated building a marine lab in the school with reef tanks, a coral research station, and a coral seed bank. They also partnered with experts from environmental science organizations such as The Reef Institute in West Palm Beach, which provided the coral for use in the project, and the Coral Restoration Foundation in the Florida Keys. Ashley recognizes how fortunate she was to be at a school where she was given the opportunity to look at science in a different way and to focus on relevant local issues, which enables the kids to understand why they're learning what they're learning.

Students were asked about their interests and were guided to contribute by using their own skill sets. One student created a 3D model for how a coral tree would work based on their design work. Others used their passion for photography and business to photograph their progress and create a merchandising plan that raised funds for coral restoration. Students with interest in communication and marketing created a ten-episode podcast series and an Instagram account. School for these kids became relevant as they tackled real-life issues with an opportunity mindset by trekking into the unknown to explore what's possible.

They understood that if the coral grew at the expected rate based on their experiments, the coral colonies could be rebuilt with the help of the Coral Restoration Foundation. This taught the younger generation that there are some problems that cannot be solved through one lens or perspective but require an integration of different subject matters, organizations, and people. And to solve a problem, we need to first identify the opportunity collaboratively and weave our collective genius by working together. Students learned the power of community in making a difference—they saw how their school supported teaching them in new ways, they saw experts generously offering help, and they experienced being part of a greater global community that came together around the shared purpose of saving the coral reefs.

Ashley and Monica offer a personal challenge for principals, teachers, students, parents, and themselves: can we unlearn what we believe teaching and learning is and trust our hearts to cocreate the systems that not only unleash the potential and imagination of students but also open healthy pathways to creating the world that is emerging, abundantly filled with possibilities? This is no easy task, because those holding on to the old programming are afraid to let go of how we have been doing things. Think about how the business of textbook publishers could be disrupted if teachers taught differently; those companies have a vested interest in the status quo that supports their current business model, which is ensuring that teachers believe they are being provided with the best gems of education.

But is it effective? We are facing a burning platform when it comes to education. For those who love facts, here they are for the United States: Gallup tells us that 56 percent of high school students are disengaged from schooling, and a study by Yale reports that 75 percent have negative feelings about school. Meanwhile, teen suicide increases by about 20 percent during the school year, returning to lower levels over summer break and holidays. This seasonal pattern stops at age eighteen, suggesting that it's the experience of schooling that causes the annual "back-to-school" uptick in teen suicides. From India to Russia, the teen suicide rate is soaring and there are many parents seeking answers for what they could have done to prevent it. There is something inherently sick in the foundation of our current education systems.

Healthy systems will not come from those in the mainstream who are fearful of exploring opportunities. It takes the ones willing to walk on the edges of possibility and bring real-world examples of igniting our youth and building holistic systems around funding and regenerative approaches. It takes great courage to see beyond problems that others are still struggling through. Visionary authors Margaret Wheatley and Deborah Frieze have this to share: "This is why it's so important that pioneers work as community, encouraging one another through the trials and risks natural to those giving birth to the new in the midst of the breakdown of the old."

Monica identified the underlying problem of not advancing in climate work as the lack of climate education grounded in systems thinking. Businesses, education, and funders are all still largely siloed: each discipline within each sector is specialized and isolated from the others. The opportunity Monica sees is no longer viewing climate change from a departmental mindset but bringing together the interconnected factors that impact the climate, environment, and social systems. When we fund climate education via systems thinking "centers" so they can support educators and trainers, we are enabling those educators to prepare a climate-literate workforce.

As a result, Monica is on a mission to launch the Dynamic Results Foundation, which will use a hybrid business model to accelerate deployment of climate education (K–12, higher education, and workforce development) via systems thinking. The goal is to change the way we educate and how we fund that change by listening to those on the front line—teachers, educators, curriculum developers, and sustainability directors—and providing the resources they need to get this mission-critical work done. Climate change is an education issue, and this foundation will fund this missing link. Monica believes that by supporting visionary teachers like Ashley and many others, her foundation will come up with the systems that will infuse the love that is needed to open pathways for the education that children around the world deeply deserve.

Can you imagine what is possible when Monica is able to cocreate holistic systems-wide programs for teachers that make it easy for them to introduce real-life experiments into the hearts of our children? I can. Operation E15 is a tested energy and environmental program at Sierra Vista High School in Nevada, an at-risk school, that was adapted to include proficiency in STEM. "I found a way out of isolation through collaboration. Partnering with Judy Treichel, executive director of the Nevada Nuclear Waste Task Force, principal Dr. John Anzalone, and AP science teacher Arlene Kam made this effort fly," Monica points out. Framed by the teacher, painted by the students, and supported by Energy Bridge, this program used real-world applications and was based on the following path: learn, apply, pass on, and communicate.

By linking education, communication, and outreach to build a resilient community, the goal was to prepare students for global change. Mya Thomsen, a student of Operation E15, didn't need to imagine it, as she experienced that "this program makes leaders for tomorrow using real-world problems. Students get hands-on experience learning from experts. No other class gives the same experience. The skills we learn are more than just science. We learn life skills." And Ashley's students learned the true purpose behind growing coral and the importance of these organisms to the ecosystem.

So, what's next for Ashley and Monica? "After visiting Dr. John Bergman this past summer, I realized how little I know about my spine. This led me to connect how little we know about the Earth to our own bodies and the consequences of ignorance. How we treat the Earth is related to how we treat our bodies. Just look at what we eat and how it's produced," Monica shares. So, while continuing to focus on climate change, the two will embark on helping teachers inspire their students to study how to build healthy immune systems.

Another exceptional visionary in education is Michael Strong. For most of the past thirty-five years, he has created small, personalized schools that attract teens escaping large, impersonal public and private schools. His most recent school, Expanse, launched in 2020, is a full middle school program for children ages ten to fourteen. It uses Socratic practice, a form of text-based intellectual dialogue, as the cornerstone of the educational experience. Unlike a traditional English class, Expanse doesn't have teachers who lead students to a particular understanding of a text or idea. Instead, the goal is to encourage students to pull out what *they* see in the texts brought to them. There are mentors and guides who provide encouragement, foster discussion among peers, and provide insight, but learning is student led.

Michael is convinced that middle school students at Expanse are often learning high school-level concepts more deeply than the vast majority of high school students. He believes that when their blood is boiling from debate and discussion, they also learn persuasive writing, which is another core skill. Students have a daily session called Community, where they share announcements, appreciations, and frustrations. Afternoons are dedicated to STEM education, for which they use QuantumCamp curriculum, followed by individual projects.

Michael's motto is "Criticize by creation." Although service has a role to play, activism has a role to play, and traditional profit-seeking business has a role to play, one of the most potent, yet underdeveloped, paths to improving the world is conscious entrepreneurship. It helps us build out a healthier world through entrepreneurial solutions to our biggest opportunities.

Dr. Igal Horowitz is an amazing human being. Not only is he the safari veterinarian and the CEO of the Israeli Wildlife Hospital at the Israel Safari in Ramat Gan, but he is also a pioneer in education. His mission is not only to heal and return to the wild the animals brought into the hospital, but to save their very species from extinction. The hospital is an outlet for education as well as being a place for medical response and treatment.

Igal brought in a team who started a school for children with learning disabilities (aged twelve and up) to study through interactive learning with animals at the Safari. The open space encourages creative thinking, initiative, and innovation. It also takes into account that many children with learning disabilities do not succeed in traditional schools and face issues of low self-esteem and failure in comparison to their peers. In this setting, the students are involved in a variety of tasks: caring for the animals, administering medicine, watching operations, and feeding; some even get an opportunity to learn accounting. The school encourages social involvement and responsibility. This type of schooling brings the children together in their deep love of animals as they are directly involved in their care. Imagine what it would be like if more of these schools emerged around the world to meet children where they are.

Zoos in the twenty-first century have been transformed from institutions whose function was to entertain the public into institutions with a significant educational and moral responsibility. Some of the most important functions of safaris today are conservation of endangered species, expanding the public's familiarity with nature and wildlife, exposing them to the dangers and challenges facing wildlife, and treatment and rehabilitation of local wildlife. As part of their education at the Safari school, students learn about native species, their conservation, and the causes of their arrival at the hospital. They also learn about worldwide endangered species and the threats facing them, as well as breeding programs whose purpose is to protect the future of these species.

Students learn the value of the preservation of nature and ultimately the preservation of ourselves as part of the animal world. The school addresses a need to find outlets for the dreams and talents of the younger generation, as well as the demand of the parents to provide their children with rich and satisfying learning experiences—something the traditional education system often has trouble providing. Igal shares, "We are answering these needs with our unique school in the midst of the Safari, which is the first of its kind in the world."

Together with experts from the Leibniz Institute for Zoo and Wildlife Research (Leibniz-IZW) in Germany, Igal has started what he calls Noah's Ark as a way to save many animals from extinction. They are using innovative techniques to create a DNA tissue bank for animals—especially those expected to become extinct in the next few years. "Noah collected all the animals and saved them from extinction years ago. I believe it is now our turn to do this," shares Igal. "In the biblical story, there was the flood and Noah saved the animals. We have a flood of people that are harming nature. The modern 'ark' is our container of liquid nitrogen." And isn't it incredible that the students get to participate and learn from science directly?

We are entering some very exciting times in human history, which include people being able to connect across the world in instantaneous ways. It is a reminder to all of us, as inventors and architects on this journey of discovery, of our responsibility to more wisely navigate the future course of our lives and be open to trusting our hearts fully. Every team mentioned here welcomes donations and collaboration from purpose-driven people who want to join forces to create what is needed most.

Even when you bend down to pick something up from the ground, there is a strategy in place for how you will do it. The less time you invest in fear and worry, the more you can spend on thinking about what you do and how you do it. Think about the times you have been proactive and fulfilled. Now, think about the times you have been reactive and stuck hesitating. What was the strategy that worked and gave you the healthiest results?

As the leader of your own life, you can become aware and clear on what you want to create in your life and work. When you see your work as your art and creation, why you are doing it becomes deeply important. Why are you here? What are you longing for?

You may have been identified all your life by your gender, status, geography, job, or another characteristic that put you in a jar with a label. Is this really how *you* want to identify? If your answer is yes, then that's healthy for you to be aware of. But if it is no, that is when the fun begins, because it is an uncomfortable place from which many of us learn to let go.

WHAT'S YOUR DOWNLOAD?
DO YOU NEED TO REBOOT?

When you are born, society starts to download knowledge into you of how life should be. You get shaped and molded so you can be societally ready. It starts in the nursery and continues throughout your schooling. You constantly receive "software downloads" to prepare for your upload as who they want you to be. For many who choose the education route, university is the first time you believe you have a choice in determining what you want to do. But you don't have a clue about who is truly making this decision. You are more focused on meeting the expectations set upon you, because you believe this will get you love. You learn that there is a reward—love and approval—if you do what is expected of you.

The reward system of our society is backward. If, as parents, we learned to reward kids when they did what *they* wanted to do, we would be encouraging young people to seek fulfillment and joy. This would help them develop and determine who they are. Children would know themselves and would value being grounded and self-aware.

Along the way, many of us get lost. It is hard to discern all the junk knowledge that fills our minds and distracts us from the truth. There are people who shout the loudest to sell their wares or increase their standing. But the generous, kind, giving, compassionate folks do not need to hide behind titles or shout from the rooftops. We simply get on and do our work without constant external validation.

Living is about having a life with deep purpose. Knowing who you are and why you are here is fundamental to creating a healthy, abundant life. Unfortunately, many today have this backward and simply focus on how they can be someone important in a society driven by power, status, and ego. It's not really anyone's fault, because that was the knowledge downloaded to them on how to succeed in life.

There is no manual for how to listen to yourself. There is no course available apart from a lot of practice and inner listening. In our world, because there seems to be a manual for how we must behave, perhaps we have forgotten to learn how to do this unassuming act of listening to our own heart so we can hear our whole self speaking to us. Trusting our heart can be simple, and yet it depends on each of us and how much practice we need to unlearn. We can stop doing what everyone expects of us and allow our self-awareness to guide us.

To listen to your body, for example, you can unlearn how you learned to eat and become more conscious of whether what you're consuming is toxic or healthy. There are certain foods I no longer consume because I listened to how my body responded in terms of feeling tired, fatigued, or depleted. I prefer to consume food that energizes me and makes me healthy in every way. When you are mistreating your body, you do not feel good. Your soul feels sad and loses its enthusiasm. Unfortunately, a lot of us have learned to numb ourselves with food so we don't have to feel.

Being conscious about the food you are putting into your mouth is a key step. Now ask yourself what thoughts you're feeding your mind and what kind of people you're surrounding yourself with. Become aware of their thoughts and opinions, because they are also feeding your mind—just like the similar foods you eat. Unlearning requires you to take the journey from being unconscious about your actions to being conscious of them and making conscious choices. You were given boundaries and limitations as part of your education in becoming a responsible adult. Being able to think and feel deeply is available to each one of us. You are capable of being in charge of yourself to discover your own truth without outside interference. There is no pill for this—it's called life!

Realizing that no one knows anything was a great source of freedom for me. You see, I am very curious and have been conditioned to seek knowledge. And one day, when I realized this one fact—that no one knows anything about how I should live my life—I started to trust myself more. If no one knows anything, how could anyone tell me how I should be? The healthiest way for me was to experiment and be as vague as I could be with some of my ideas to see what questions people would ask me.

Can you trust that your crazy idea or way of life has merit and be willing to experiment and keep going (what's called "failing" in our current reality) until you get it? You don't know which way it will go until you try. The most powerful step you can ever take is the first one. Make a decision, stop doing something, create something, test something, try something. Learn for yourself if your idea is a good one.

You can sit back and believe that your life sucks, or you can go explore what is possible for you. And if you care about your life, you will realize that life doesn't suck but that maybe on some days your attitude does. And that's okay if you want to live in that world. But your opportunity is to realize that no one has your answers. Testing an idea will teach you more than spending time spinning it in your mind. I learned whom to trust and whom not to trust by learning to trust myself and meeting a lot of people who tried to sell me their answers.

Hope is alive and available to each of us. It flourishes at the beginning of change, transformation, and creation. You just need to clear the way to spark your imagination. The journey of life takes us through a range of experiences to see how we respond to changing situations. It's like a video game with challenges that come to test you and see how you deal with unexpected obstacles and perceived attacks. You keep repeating the same scenario and situations until you learn enough to go to the next level. You don't have to relive the past to achieve—only understand the game and improve your skills to go on and be challenged by another set of obstacles. When you are not invested in the outcome, you open yourself up to receive more information and to welcome the unknown.

Everything teaches you. We are on this path called life that has many twists and turns. Every step you take and every attitude and mindset you adopt can change your life. If you take a big risk and it does not turn out the way you expected, you can be riddled with guilt, humiliation, and shame for months, until you realize it was just an exercise you were supposed to learn from. Some of the lessons that come to us are what we need to learn at that moment whether we like it or not. The quicker you can grasp this concept, the easier it will be for you to "get back on the horse."

If you fear potential situations, you will get stuck and miss out on other opportunities. It is so easy to buy into fear and let it destroy your experiences. It's not your fault. It's not personal. It is life ebbing and flowing. It's easy to get lost and immersed in fear. It surrounds us every minute of every day, blasted ad nauseam by the news, media, advertising, shows, and our immediate environment. But we get to choose whether we want to invite it in. This is how prevalent it is: research shows that people fear uncertainty more than physical pain.

Self-development takes us out of our comfort zone, a place of certainty, and puts us on an unknown, virgin path. While most of us become students at the age of six or seven, we do not face our true relationship with life until much later. Imagine if more people shared their highs and lows and how much these impacted their experience as an adventurer and explorer.

In an interview published in *Scientific American* in October 2008, Professor Joseph LeDoux stated, "When you see the stock market fall 1,000 points, that's the same as seeing a snake." LeDoux, professor of neuroscience and psychology at the Center for Neural Science at New York University, also commented, "Fear is the response to the immediate stimuli. The empty feeling in your gut, the racing of your heart, palms sweating, nervousness—that's your brain responding in a preprogrammed way to a very specific threat … Since our brains are programmed to be similar in structure, we can assume that what I experience when I'm threatened is something similar to what you experience." A number of species are also affected in similar ways by fear. "We come into the world knowing how to be afraid, because our brains have evolved to deal with nature," said LeDoux. The interviewer noted that "the brains of rats and humans respond in similar ways to threats, even though the threat itself might be completely different."

Getting out of your comfort zone can radically change your course. If you live in constant fear, you need to understand where the fear stems from. Why do so many people fear something that's unknown? How do you want to experience life? Fear, to a certain degree, is our way of being a bit self-indulgent. How can we be too scared to try something when we don't know how we will react to it?

I refuse to spend my life in irrational fear. I'd rather face the challenges of making what I believe in happen than stay stuck in irrational fear. And this is coming from a place of knowing. I have experienced many scary situations in my life, but I faced them and I am still here. When you sit down and record your fears, you will understand that 90 percent of them are irrational. You have to ask yourself if they are a real threat or if you spend your imagination creating them and making them real!

♥ What is your biggest fear right now? Name it. Write it down.
♥ Look at it. *Really* look at it.
♥ What scares you so much that you are willing to risk everything by letting it paralyze you and keep you where you are?

- ♥ Does it make you feel safe?
- ♥ Or is that an illusion or a delusion?
- ♥ What happens when you take in this new meaning of safety?
- ♥ Is playing it safe making you happy or making you unhappy?
- ♥ You can admire someone else for being bold and worship or envy them. Let them inspire you to discover why are you here and what your mission is.
- ♥ Is your fear a real threat or an imagined one?

Very, very rarely do we honestly have a reason to live in a state of irrational fear. Fear can motivate us to make sure the things that scare us never happen. As a conscious leader of your life, you can figure out how to disengage from the stress and use it as an ally.

When you trust yourself fully, it allows you to trust others because you know when something is healthy or unhealthy and are able to act accordingly. When there is trust, there is no longer energy wasted in questioning motivations, decisions, or actions. You just listen to your intuition to guide you. When there are hiccups along the road, you trust in your circle to share and participate in solutions and to help you overcome any paralyzing fears. If you can't entrust your dreams to others, you will find it incredibly challenging to cocreate.

The current environment fosters the blame game, which has perpetuated and become a feeding frenzy. It has been medically proven that trauma often gets passed from one generation to another, just like DNA. So it is imperative that we stop this insane cycle of blaming others. We can carry trauma from our parents and ancestors and will continue to do so unless we consciously decide to detach and let it go. The wounds run deep, but we didn't come here to continue the victimhood or martyrdom. We actually came here to create and orchestrate a new architectural structure and to face the challenges and embrace all the opportunities.

You are imperfect and perfect the way you are; you don't need to strive for an unrealistic bar of perfection, always trying to be better, falling short and not feeling satisfied with who you are. Everyone makes mistakes, including your parents. You came equipped with everything you need, and it is up to you to tap into these resources and the lessons you came here to learn. It is as simple as knowing how to ask for help, or offering to help someone, and finding answers and insights through helping each other, even if we don't yet know we need it. Alan Watts gives us this bit of wisdom: "This is the real secret of life—to be completely engaged with what you are doing in the here and now. And instead of calling it work, realize it is play."

EXPEDITION 26

YOUR INSIDE JOB IS WAITING

♥

How often do you drive down the highway and decide to take a certain lane, thinking it will be the faster route, only to discover that the other lane is now running smoother and your new lane is stop-and-go? What about at the grocery store when you hop from line to line, each time hoping this one will go faster than the others? To add to your frustration, you find yourself behind someone who can't find their checkbook and is delaying your progress even more while you stand there wondering why anyone still uses checks.

Do you get irritated and reprimand yourself for making a bad decision, or do you realize that this lane belongs to you? Perhaps this opportunity is providing you with a lesson beyond the choices you make—perhaps it's testing you to see what you have learned so far. The destination is not as important as the path—and this is your path.

You can take a similar approach when it comes to envy. So many people focus on and pine for what others have, completely unappreciative of what they themselves already have. The more grateful you are for the small things, the more things will show up for you to be grateful for, because gratefulness opens you up to receive more. It doesn't matter if you are beautiful and rich, handsome and successful—spend time with the rich and beautiful and you will uncover their insecurities. All dreams and successes are mixed with courage and insecurities.

Recognize that every person has their own path in life, including siblings and other family members, and everyone has to face their own challenges, demons, and insecurities with their own nemeses. It's up to you to accept your past and know that it's a springboard to where you find yourself at each junction of your life.

The key to life is to maintain your well-being, which absolutely includes your emotional, mental, and physical health. Happiness and joy are available to all, as much as jealousy and anger. Understanding the challenges and opportunities of your personal navigation system helps you to steer your ship. When you are searching outside of yourself for recognition or validation, you will most likely be disappointed. This can lead to jealousy or feeling that you're not good enough or fearing that you're missing out. Your search for wholeness is an inside job. Wanting endorsement from outside of yourself or seeking external events or things that you think will make you happy, will most likely make you unhappier.

Recall the happiest moment in your life—were you walking on the beach, observing whales, hiking in the mountains, planting a garden, having a meaningful conversation, being there for the birth of your child, launching a project, spending time alone? Remember the feelings that enveloped you. There was an all-knowingness that it was meant to be and everything had come into alignment at that very moment. The gratitude was overwhelming because it had so much meaning, and you just knew you were truly listening to the whispers of your heart. The certainty of knowing brings a sense of peace and calm—it is in the palm of your hand. It is not necessary to keep searching or seeking externally for the peace and calm, because it exists within. You cannot seek a sense of wholeness, because it is about finding the different pieces and parts of yourself that have been separated or are in conflict. You can only gather them and bring them into inner balance and harmony. This is definitely something that is not taught in school. Happiness comes from creating and sharing ourselves.

You can only truly give and receive from a place of knowing you are whole. When you become whole within yourself, you have a deep-seated knowingness that it is absolutely safe to give and share. You can never give away a piece of yourself or jeopardize who you are, because it already belongs to you. It does not come from an outside force. It comes through you. True joy is sharing your happiness with others and experiencing their appreciation in receiving, but this cannot be done without knowing your wholeness first.

DO YOU EVER FEEL LIKE YOU NEED TO PROVE YOURSELF?

Life is a classroom with no windows or doors. It is up to you to design the openings and doorways for yourself and to join by jumping into the flow. When you connect with others and come together to create, you are putting forth your trust, and in turn they are trusting in you. Whether it's business or personal, there is a dependency created in the agreement. You are signing up to play a specific role in their life. Life is making the statement that you have been chosen as the right person to fulfill certain tasks. If this agreement involves a monetary exchange, the expectations increase, and this can put more pressure on you to prove your ability to deliver.

It makes no difference whether it's a business contract or becoming a parent or spouse, you have signed up officially to interact and participate in the life of another, however temporarily. Your thoughts and actions impact their lives too. The more important the relationship is, the more responsibility that comes with this promise.

Imagine you're writing a book for people who are ready for what you have to share. This means you will be impacting souls who want to learn how to imagine and create new paths in the world. You are here to encourage anyone who is ready to trek into the unknown to plant seeds. It is not just an opportunity to show up with a task and an initiative; it demonstrates that great trust has been placed in you to provide healthy tools to help with the evolution of others' lives and the community. If you show up to prove how smart you are or how ingenious the book is, you will be driving in with your ego and more than likely the book will fail in the long run. The real success of the book will happen when you can shift your mindset to the impact, the ripples you will be creating in individual lives, families, and communities. Let go and trust—the book will grow and evolve by itself to a greater extent when you release control, and then it can provide benefits beyond anything you could imagine. This way you will be able to build great trust that will continue to sustain and magnify in many ways.

You can grow and learn by challenging yourself through helping others, and at the same time build your own self-esteem and track record as you create. You also serve as an inspiration for others who doubt, creating new paths for them to unleash. Helping ourselves encourages us to help others too—much is possible and abundant. Shifting your focus to dream about the impact you want to have requires letting go of the need to prove yourself and bringing forth your talents to make it happen. Don't get discouraged if some things don't work out; at least you know you tried, and you can apply any lessons and insights as you continue to grow and experiment.

In our current society, many of us have learned to hide our failures. People talk about them behind closed doors, trying to cloak their imperfections. What if we started including failure studies in the curriculum of our educational systems? Aren't failures valuable life lessons that can foster a great deal of knowledge and expertise? Isn't using failure as a learning tool much better than suppressing it in shame?

Leaders in some nonprofit organizations have started "Fail Fairs," where they openly share their failures so others can learn and talk about the lessons they gained. In different parts of the world, people are getting together for what they call "Fuck Up Night." It's a time for people to talk openly about their failures. You learn that no one is perfect and everyone needs to do their own work. Have you ever seen a five-year-old learn how to ride a bicycle without falling off, no matter how skilled they were? To ride a bike, you need the right balance and a lot of practice. Even with scraped elbows and bruised knees, the child gets up and tries again.

EXPERIENCING WHAT'S BEHIND THE DOOR

No one likes to be disoriented. No one wants to feel lost. Many who have been programmed to plan for the future or document the past have lost the art of being spontaneous and in the moment. We need to remember how to imagine and develop alternatives and be open to different possibilities and approaches.

Do you remember the last time you were stressed out, angry, and blaming everyone for something crazy that happened to you? What were you angry about? Who did you blame for it? Do you even remember what it was about? Or are you in the midst of a drama right now? Stop for a minute and reflect on it. What really happened? Stick to the facts only. Breathe. Notice where you are feeling powerless. Are you playing the role of the victim or the villain, or can you step in with your red cape and superpowers and play the hero?

One of the lessons I learned is to distinguish between being a victim and becoming aware of when I was being bullied. I started questioning everything. Universal law teaches us that unconditional love does not require us to be the object of abuse. Sometimes people or situations appear so you can learn to put yourself first and step into your power. It is an opportunity to learn how to love and have more compassion, so you can forgive yourself and move on. When you are smack in it, you can't see or think clearly as you are swept into the injustice and unfairness that you feel is happening. It feels like a deep black hole that keeps getting deeper and wider. In time and with practice, you will be able to stand up and look down into the hole and see that it was never really that deep, only a pothole to trip over so you could learn to be whole.

When you can forgive yourself first and let go of things that gnaw at you with guilt, or when you can forgive someone you believe has wronged you, you heal yourself. There is no reason to stay stuck in anger, resentment, or fear. You need only grow and evolve, and it takes a lot of work.

Forgiving someone who has harmed you is not condoning their actions or saying what they did was okay. Imagine how much energy you're wasting playing the tape over and over again in your head about what happened. These experiences that are harmful often hold you hostage. What useful purpose does it serve to keep telling the same story of hurt with no resolution?

The world is filled with hurtful energy that has not been forgiven or released. This energy is particularly strong in those who see themselves as victims and not as creators. As a victim, it is easy to blame others or a structure outside yourself, and it can be challenging to forgive those who have wronged you. When you realize that nothing can happen to you without your permission, you can take responsibility for your creations and do something about them. In reality, forgiveness heals you and those around you.

When something in the past is forgiven, it ripples through the present and into the future. Forgiveness is about learning how to let go and move on. It is not easy, but when you realize the stress and anxiety created by staying in these stories, and when you can see that they're causing more harm to you and your health, it's time to start deconstructing them. Break down the story piece by piece, and see what you can learn and benefit from. Let go of what is holding you back and jump back into the flow of life with your heart.

Once you forgive someone—including yourself—compassion will flow. It allows you to get to the root cause and see what actually happened and why. It does not mean that what was done was okay, but it allows for understanding and awareness so you can find the hidden gift in what happened. Maybe now your radar can more easily be tuned to spot someone approaching with an unhealthy agenda.

Words and promises are not enough to sustain trustworthy relationships. Empty words are simply that—empty. How you treat yourself matters because you get to learn who and what is healthy and unhealthy for you. Actions truly speak louder than the words of someone's philosophy.

The deeper question is, do you want to stay in a story that continues to hurt you or do you want to heal, learn how you *do* have the capacity to forgive, and walk in new shoes so they can no longer harm you?

It takes conscious awareness to break a harmful, habitual practice. It is possible when you are willing to have the intention of healing. Each of us can stop dwelling on how we were wronged or deceived. We can consciously decide not to play the victim by moving on with our life. We can also try to understand the root cause of why we were harmed by imagining what it would be like to be them. Then we can let go of them and the story entirely if we want to, or we can choose to reconcile. It is something I have been practicing and playing with, since I don't want to carry my pain and hurt with me everywhere I go. When I began this practice, it was hard. But as I started to observe my own role and understand the root causes, it became easier. And as we experienced in *F*ck the Bucket List for the Soul*, dealing with ancestral trauma, which we each carry to varying degrees, can be the beginning of releasing ourselves and cutting the cords of our deep trauma.

When you see the world as your playground, you can practice and experiment by taking small steps to build your personal navigation system and your confidence. Maybe you can prove to yourself that you can accomplish things you didn't truly believe you could. It is always healthy to start with small dreams and explore your own boundaries.

There is no need to limit yourself when you are here to imagine, experiment, and create. How can you effect change if you are not willing to throw yourself into the ring? When you can free yourself of others' definitions of success, you can take off the blindfold and shackles and take a real leap of faith.

Think about it. It's a hot summer day and you're having a great time relaxing and enjoying yourself. You decide to stop by the homemade ice cream shop and get a custom-made ice cream, just the way you like it. You choose the type of milk you want, the flavors, and the toppings. You stand there watching as they make it just for you. In anticipation, you imagine what it will taste like and then salivate over your first bite. You went from imagining that taste to actually experiencing it.

WHEN YOU SEE LIFE AS AN ADVENTURE, MUCH IS POSSIBLE

Your outlook on life matters. Your mindset is one of your most precious resources, because it opens the window of your world. When you see everything as a problem, you will encounter many problems that distract you or stop you in your tracks. When you are willing to see many opportunities, you will have the mindset of a creator—someone who has the power to make things happen.

It's exciting to explore possibilities. It is still amazing that you can board a plane in one part of the world and in a few hours land in another country that you have never experienced. What is exciting is the journey, not the destination. What can be created through this journey of flying to another place in the world? You are no longer a tourist, but a purposeful adventurer and a meaningful creator.

The travel industry is set up to sell illusions through enticing images of beautiful, exotic people drinking cocktails by the pool or running on sandy beaches or boardwalks. Their business is to create a fantasy that you will often dream about experiencing. Ask anyone to describe what a trip to Hawaii or Fiji would feel like and you will see how successful the travel industry has been in providing images for these destinations. It is a figment of your imagination to travel somewhere to be someone you are not.

You can choose your own path, or you can have your path constructed for you. It's always a choice. What if more people traveled for their souls, and not for the latest fashion trends perceived by their eyes? What happens when you listen to your heart and soul for guidance? What kind of experiences will you have? What people will you find on your path?

When you travel a lot, you realize that horizons stop being a geographic location. They take on a different dimension. Taking a trip to fulfill your soul's mission crosses the horizon of your imagination. Geographic locations may simply be opportunities to gain new perspectives and revelations through the experience of different cultures and traditions. These encounters bring new insight and understanding that feed your soul to become more whole and help you find ways to lift and shift yourself and others.

THE HEART OF AN ARTIST

Bruce Lee, renowned martial artist and founder of the martial art Jeet Kune Do, was an artist who pursued truth and beauty using his physical and emotional body as art. He said, "I have always been a martial artist by choice and an actor by profession. But, above all, I am hoping to actualize myself to be an artist of life along the way...I don't know what is the meaning of death, but I am not afraid to die. And I go on, non-stop, going forward, even though I, Bruce Lee, may die some day without fulfilling all of my ambitions, I will have no regrets. I did what I wanted to do and what I've done, I've done with sincerity and to the best of my ability. You can't expect much more from life."

The term "artist" calls up mental images that we all have implanted in our psyche; the term "salesman" does as well. Each of these roles conjures an image in our mind and a feeling in our gut. Some of us see artists as creative geniuses working in seclusion. We've been taught that to be creative, we must work in silence and unveil our masterpiece or launch our book to an audience who will ultimately determine the actual worth of our creations. What image comes to your mind when you think of a salesman? Unlike artists, most salespeople are paid by commission and their worth is determined by how much they sell. They will appear on a list recognizing them as the best when they bring in the highest sales for their organization. Their art is their ability to convince consumers to buy from them, and when they believe in the value of what they are selling, they tap into their art.

It used to be that artists could focus on creating, whether a painting or a book or a musical composition. But for independent authors like myself, the expectation is that we master marketing, since we don't have huge publishing budgets behind us. If you decide to write a book, you will most likely hear experts telling you to spend a year building your author platform, as it's more important than your book. This advice points you in the direction of finding influencers and the dying marketing machine dictating to you how to find your audience. This provides an interesting challenge for those of us who have walked away from the manual of success to connect with those ready for what we have to offer.

When you cook a healthy meal, you select nutritious ingredients and then spend time weaving them together to create an experience—the meal. If you have invited others to share in the meal, you get to see firsthand how they respond to your craft of cooking. But when I spent months and months writing this trilogy, what motivated me most was the impact the words would have on every person they would touch. The artist within me sprinkled the pages with my desire for more people around the world to discover our own wonder, trek into the unknown, and trust our heart. I have confidence that when we're doing our own work and are healthy to the core, we can coproduce a healthy world. It gets me excited to know that planting seeds can help you thrive and not suffer through your life. Maybe one day I can sit and watch people's reactions to my art. But until then, I have to rely on hearing back from you through an online review, email, or mention. I struggle with traditional marketing and hope that as more people experience these books, we can talk about what's in them and the impact they've had on us. I am sure we all have an artist within us with a deep desire to follow our heart.

Revered by generations as the greatest martial artist in popular culture, Bruce Lee's art and poetry continue to inspire the awakening of generations. He writes, "By martial art I mean, like any art, an unrestricted expression of our individual soul … The human soul is what interests me. I live to express myself freely in creation."

IMAGINING POSSIBILITIES

We're witnessing exponential growth in the understanding of and alternative treatments for depression, loneliness, and anxiety, despite the fact that mental illness has been stigmatized for decades. Almost 2.5 million prescriptions for Prozac were written as far back as 1988, the year after its approval by the FDA. What has been happening since then is that more of us do not want to be medicated by the pharmaceutical industry and are looking for alternative ways to heal.

Because of our celebrity culture, it has helped many people feel less alone when they see people they admire speak openly about their own struggles. My cousin Stephen Fry disclosed his battles in the BBC documentary *The Secret Life of the Manic Depressive*, and since then, he's openly discussed his struggle with his illness and his suicide attempts. I watched the film while visiting his parents in the United Kingdom, and I was glad I could be close by as he discussed the "morbid" seriousness of his disease, which he compares to having "your own personal weather." In dealing with it, he says, there are "two mistakes … to deny that it's raining … and to say, 'therefore my life is over. It's raining and the sun will never come out.'" The more we openly discuss our sadness and the trauma we carry, the more we understand that there's healthy medicine available that doesn't always come in a tablet.

There is no quick fix for mental illness and no catchall solution, which is why I want to share with you the passion of Ahad Bandealy, who is not only a visionary but a leader with a huge heart. He loves people and cares deeply about being of service to humanity. When he sets out to do something, he gives it everything he has and focuses on outcomes and how they will impact the lives of people who need help. Everyone struggles with their mental health and well-being, but it can be difficult to reach out for support. Get A-Head® was created by a team of mental health experts to combat some of the barriers we face in getting care, which include anonymity, accessibility, immediacy, and relatability. When Ahad first shared his vision with me, he told me that university students in crisis sometimes have to wait six months to get help, so he was building an app that would connect clinicians with students immediately. With the soaring suicide rates and increasing depression and anxiety in the world, his is a healthy system that is now helping not only students but also musicians, athletes, and employees. As the cofounder, he is not only building the platform but is also securing investment that would allow it to be there for the people who need it most.

What's remarkable about Ahad is that he transformed his vision with the aid of his team to build a platform that supports people who are struggling and need help. It's changing the landscape of mental health forever by providing e-counseling for those in need of support and affordable, stigma-free access to care. The use of AI and machine language layered into the technology's analytics places Get A-Head® at the forefront of the emerging world. It is helping to provide healing and support during uncertain times. Ahad's plan to integrate tools such as music therapies, sound healing, and podcasts are so needed in today's environment. And for me, there is no reason to feel hopeless when there are so many amazing people around us creating a healthier world.

And guess what? We are all connected in mysterious ways—ways they never teach you in school. How many times have you had a déjà vu moment, like walking down the street and feeling as if you just saw someone you know, but you *know* you don't really know them and there is no chance you are connected. Where does that feeling come from? There is a deeper meaning that we don't always understand. It is easier to study and learn about what is visible; the invisible is a great challenge. Our Western culture has conditioned many to be addicted to material things and to place the most importance on the material world. In truth, the invisible has more power, and it's the invisible bars that jail and torment us. There is no official course in school teaching us how we can break free from them.

We don't know how the wires are connected between us, and yet we know we are all connected. We all share the same destiny because we share the same world, and there are consequences to all of this. The world is a beautiful and miraculous place, and with the many missteps made by man, we have mistreated our home. Yet there is still an opportunity to clean up the mess we have made. Polluted air, contaminated oceans, broken people, and tainted soil didn't just happen. Hunger, homelessness, and war continue to ravish our planet and suppress and oppress our innate drive for peace and tranquility. However, we don't have to remain stuck in problems and continue to create more. It's time for healthy leaders to see the opportunities to step up and connect, to work together on the challenging changes these situations require. We cannot believe that everything will somehow magically be okay without having to do any work ourselves. This idea has brought us to a pivotal, unprecedented breaking point in human history.

We now know that if there is a massive oil spill in some other part of the world, it will ultimately impact our own water supply, because the tides and ocean currents will eventually wash it ashore. We are all connected. The financial markets clearly show that financial stability is dependent on the world banks and international stock exchanges that sustain our current economic systems. People are finally waking up to the fact that our health is jeopardized by the prioritizing of business profitability. Thankfully, more people are reading product packaging to confirm that no toxic ingredients were used. More of us are making healthier and more conscious choices as we become more aware and awake.

Over the years, we haven't just poisoned our bodies by eating too much unhealthy food or breathing polluted air, we have also polluted our minds with unhealthy thoughts and invited unhealthy people into our hearts. It is the pollution of our minds that needs our attention, so that we can change our faulty beliefs. We need a revolution in the mindset of humanity, which begins with each and every one of us.

We can't keep walking in circles, pretending that magic dust will solve our biggest problems. Our opportunity is to be proactive and do our own work, knowing that the invisible ripples will impact all of us in some way.

What happens when we live in a world where we don't care about its maintenance? This is why our mindset matters. We are all tenants in the same house, so it matters what everyone does. We live in a world where it takes a split second to connect to someone else through technology and social platforms. We are much more connected than we can imagine, so it is important to be aware of our impact through bad behavior and habits. It doesn't matter whether it's being played out on the global stage or within the spheres of our own private lives—the ripple effect is felt on the other side of the world.

EXPEDITION 27

TRUSTING YOUR
INTERNAL GUIDANCE

L ife gives us what we can handle, even though we sometimes don't believe we can deal with the twists and turns along our path. How we choose to navigate lies in our hearts and is manifest through the choices we make and the energy we expend. Before the days of GPS navigation, people would stop and ask someone for directions when they got lost. I hope by now you have taken out your own compass so you can map out your own route using your own operating system. Be careful not to remain stuck waiting for instructions and hanging out on the sidelines watching life go by.

Some of us have been so beaten down that we stay stuck in our problems or traumas. But there is always an opportunity to explore what's around the corner, whenever we are ready. We each hold the key and the power to set ourselves free from a world that tries to make us like everyone else. A crisis is an opportunity designed to shatter the rigid patterns of behavior trapped inside us. Sometimes we need to be shaken to the core of our being before we are willing to change. Once it happens, it is up to us to learn from the experience. Can you recall your last crisis? Do you see how you can use it now to show up in a healthier way, free of the blame and shame of the incident? What patterns or beliefs are waiting for you to shake them up?

The path is open and freely accessible to each of us. Don't fall for the fallacy that someone else has the answers for you. As with any journey, the key is to begin. It doesn't really matter where—there is no perfect entry point. When you have the mindset and curiosity of an adventurer, your world will be far easier to steer through, as you know there will be trials and errors along the way. You will be alert to the lows so that they won't be so low, and the highs won't be too high, so you can find balance on the middle path with harmony. Wisdom from aviation pioneer Amelia Earhart tells us that "the most difficult thing is the decision to act, the rest is merely tenacity. The fears are paper tigers. You can do anything you decide to do. You can act to change and control your life; and the procedure, the process is its own reward."

Change can happen when you integrate your clarity of purpose with your whole self, to be fully present to create what you want in the world. Part of the process is putting your own signature on how you want to break patterns that no longer serve you. In a noisy world where attention is a sought-after currency, standing out and being heard can be a real challenge, but it is also an opportunity to find out how powerful and effective you can be. Once you have clarity on how you want to show up and a willingness to experiment, then you can create with conviction.

In both life and work, there are codes of acceptance that you adopt. You may have been brought up to believe that you need certain codes to give you access to the doors of success. But by tuning into your inner self and following your intuition and heart—whether it's noticing when you come alive or how you're truly feeling—you can develop a stronger sense of who you are and where you need to head next.

WHAT HAPPENS WHEN YOU PUT AWAY YOUR SOMEDAY LIST?

Asking yourself new and thought-provoking questions that may at first feel uncomfortable is a way to begin. It is a great gift to understand why a situation or a person makes you feel uneasy. Going deeper to the root to grasp this will help you see what makes you *you*. If right now, in this very moment, you could start or stop anything, and there were no limitations, do you know what you would want to create and why? If you don't have a clue, be patient with yourself, stay open, and take the time to keep asking questions. Continue to delve within and understand what is hiding deep in your roots until you uncover the gem (or the pain).

How many people look forward to working in their garden every year, and how many wait until they retire to garden? It takes imagination, creativity, time, and work to plan and harvest a garden, much like building a neighborhood in a new division of a city. It takes years to establish a garden rich with vegetables, fruit trees, beautiful foliage, and blooming flowers. You also have to be prepared for the weeds, the deer, and the slugs that want to share in your bounty. The same ingredients are needed for creating anything in life. It all begins with a seed, then nourishment with organic soil, sunshine, and water—all sprinkled with love—before you're able to feast on the abundance you've created.

You need to know what materials are required, how much money you'll need, and an estimation of how much effort it will take. When it comes to transforming areas of your life, you may think you can't afford to do it now because of money, time, or obligations. But you can apply this same model and split your dreams into smaller segments. This will keep you from feeling overwhelmed by the enormity of the plan and allow you to recognize you have already used this approach in the past. You will have a better awareness of what worked and what didn't. As in a garden, some seeds don't sprout but others will. Understand why and nurture them in their own way, never giving up.

Many people spend hours and hours playing as avatars in video games, trying to win and come in first. Why would you become a champion of video games and not use the same determination and persistency in the real world to do something for yourself? It is good to become aware of times when you tell yourself you can't do something and times when you give yourself permission to be playful.

If you find it hard to play well with others, be discerning about the battles to pick. It is futile to try to change others. The only person you can change is yourself. No one can *make* you angry, if you think about it rationally. The anger or rage comes from within you. You really are in control of how you react to situations and people that cross your path. Of course, it is only natural that someone else can easily trigger anger in you, but how you choose to respond is entirely up to you.

This is your life. Your time. Your story. How you choose to invest your precious resources like your energy, your love, your compassion, and your anger, is under your command. It doesn't matter if you are steeped in wealth or completely lacking in funds; the biggest factor determining your path is always your mindset, your attitude. Curiosity keeps the dream alive and determines the direction the wind blows for you.

WHAT'S YOUR RELATIONSHIP WITH LIFE?

Whenever you turn to anyone who claims to be an expert for guidance, know that they cannot possibly have the absolute right answers for you. They are not inside your head, nor have they walked in your shoes, so they can't possibly know the battles that go on in your mind. The only person who has the healthy answers is you. And when you need them, there are qualified professionals to help you. But do your research and trust your heart to see whether you resonate with them. Only you know the risks you're willing to take and the opportunities you want to pursue. We often take pills without knowing what ails us. Likewise, it is important to perform due diligence to determine your own self-help wisdom. Then you can prescribe your own cure to put you on your own path, which includes the people you invite in.

Believing that there is a perfect solution or a better practice to follow will only get in your way. If you're a baker, for example, the lessons you learn will make you a better baker. The more you practice and experiment with different recipes to produce more varieties of breads, cakes, or pastries, the more confident you will be to trust yourself and continue on your path. And when someone enjoys your creations, it encourages you to experiment more in possibilities. It sparks a fire within you to keep celebrating your talents and gifts. Too many have lost their passion and curiosity. There's always a fear of failure attached to not being good enough, for example. Who trampled on your passion? It's time to find it again and bring it back into your life so it can be part of your natural growth and propel you forward.

Our perceived comfort zone is debilitating to the psyche, especially in a daily routine like traveling back and forth to work. If the train or subway is delayed, we get frustrated, even if we are told an emergency has occurred on the line. Our plans have been disrupted because our arrival time has changed. Change happens every time your expectations are interrupted. You will benefit greatly if you can become more aware of your comfort zone and expectations, and you will navigate a smoother path when you are aware of your reactions and resistance.

There are two key elements that help create a healthier relationship with change: considering what it means to be the captain of your ship and the navigator of your life, and knowing what is rooted in reality that you do not have control over. You are at the mercy of the forces of change, but know there is a higher purpose for the change yet to be determined, which will reveal itself in due course.

We have all experienced waking up suddenly from a deep sleep, not sure what sound woke us. We take our time coming to and getting up, until we realize that our alarm did not go off. It's late, we've overslept. We start to panic. This is what it's like when reality gives us a wake-up call—we panic. We throw logic out the window and operate out of fear. Someone else is calling the shots for where we need to be, and we fear missing whatever is on our calendar.

We spend a lifetime trying to correct the damage created by others, when the opportunity is to be our own best leader, the one our life deserves. How many times in life are you going to ignore your wake-up call? It's up to you to set your own alarm clock.

Many books end up on the shelves of personal home libraries having never been opened, experienced, or read. It is understandable, then, that the owners don't look inside themselves either—they are focused on the wrappers and jackets that the outside world sees. They adorn themselves but don't open their own covers to explore what nuggets are buried within. They miss out on all their own facets and dimensions. Like their valuable book collection, they often remain on the shelf to be admired and observed.

We've been led to believe that life should be a certain way, and we keep running in endless circles. The current state of our society is clearly dragging us down instead of freeing us to do what is possible. We can only break free of the chains of conditioning when we see the traps, seductions and addictions that are infecting our well-being.

Is it time to get in touch with a deeper purpose your heart yearns to explore and experience? Your navigation system will pop up when you become aware and listen to your body and your feelings. Stay alert to your thoughts and whether they are your own. Can you hear what your heart is telling you? What about the whispers of your soul? Opportunity is knocking to encourage you to dive into a deep heart-to-heart conversation with yourself. Then you can start to connect heart-to-heart with others.

Many people invest a lot of time, money, and energy in decorating and renovating their home and readying it to entertain guests. So many homeowners have a living room that rarely gets used. It is only for special occasions and is not really lived in. Be careful if you use your home as a showcase for others to admire, such as using the best china only for special visitors or taking the plastic covers off the furniture only when the "right" people come to visit.

TAP INTO YOUR POWER AND ACCESS YOUR TRUE VOICE

We live in a world of self-professed philosophers, life coaches, self-help gurus, and thought leaders who claim to have the answers to all of life's troubles if you'll only buy into their solution. Our conditioning has taught us to easily give away our power to others who are better suited to make decisions on our behalf. Laws and systems have been created for the lowest common denominator as a way to protect us and keep us safe. And yet, look at our world and start questioning everything. When you do, you will discover that fear and division are a foundational building block of our reality, and this no longer suits our emerging consciousness.

The moment we start looking to someone else to solve our problems, we give away our power. The path of self-discovery, which is personal, has turned into a multibillion-dollar industry offering workshops, retreats, seminars, books, and courses to help billions of people suffering from anxiety, depression, and posttraumatic stress disorder (PTSD). The US alone spent $446 billion in 2016 on medications, which is almost half of the global market. These statistics and data clearly show that there are a lot of unhappy people in the world and a lot of companies prospering from our collective unhappiness.

As we have previously explored, spirituality has become big business. When the East met the West, it all became integrated in the over-consumerism corporate mandate with franchises popping up in the fitness, meditation, and yoga industries. The self-help book market on diet, exercise, and mindfulness has exploded, launching the careers of high-profile personalities as part of the overextended consumption game. The purity of yoga and meditation has been lost in this frenetic wave of seeking perfection and fulfillment. Weeklong retreat workshops in five-star spiritual resorts, from Northern California to Costa Rica, will set you back anywhere from $1,800 to $15,000. There are many online courses and streaming workshops available to those on smaller budgets. It's up to you to practice discernment and connect with what resonates with you rather than what's popular and trendy.

Unfortunately, the underlying message of this industry steers you away from believing in yourself by telling you to trust that everyone else has your answers before you can realize your own questions and your own truth. Your inner home is not made up of *stuff*. It is a highly sophisticated machine that is very much aware. Its highly tuned sensory organs work in perfect harmony in your body, gently interacting with your heart, mind, and soul—whispering to you every second of the day. This is your own personal navigation system that allows either healthy or toxic people to approach, determines the right diet and exercise regimen, and knows what is best to sustain and maintain itself. By staying conscious, you will be able to observe the results of your choices and, over time, notice how the unhealthy options bring infections and disease into your life.

By being responsible for your health and welfare, you will be able to answer the questions for yourself and reside in your own "home" without having to pay rent to the self-professed expert that seems to have stepped in to sublet your own home to you. Are these companies, governments, and experts taking over the role of landlord when you are in charge of your own health? Do you know your true home—yourself—is rent- and mortgage-free and your inner navigation system has the ability to guide you from sadness to joy? How can we experience unconditional love unless we can give it to ourselves first?

A lot happens when we release the illusion that happiness is an external, objective goal that can be purchased. The constant pursuit of happiness is unrealistic in many ways. Joy, like pain, is free and available to every person on this planet when they are open to embracing it and welcoming it into their home. When do you realize that you are not broken, weak, or incomplete? You are human and you are enough just as you are right now. What will your home look like? Poet Mary Oliver wrote in her *Thirst* collection, "Someone I loved once gave me a box full of darkness. It took me years to understand that this, too, was a gift."

All of us have work to do in dealing with our darkness and the shadows it projects into our lives. And when there is light inside our home, we uncover the wisdom within ourselves. Too often, we don't see or we choose not to see what is right in front of us. When we can't see clearly, we are not aware of what is surrounding us. Sometimes we even refuse to wear the glasses we have been prescribed, so life remains blurry and out of focus.

All the tools you need are inside of you, when you choose to connect with yourself. Your mind holds a lot for you, and, as we explored earlier, you can choose to see a situation as either a problem or an opportunity. Check in with your heart—it will give you the signal when you are ready to accept and see reality for what it is, right in front of you. It's always there waiting for you, ready to begin.

Sometimes the mind has the capacity to take action when the heart is saying no because it is afraid or hesitant. You can spend years building layers and layers of insulation around your heart to prevent action and dialogue with yourself. But unless you are willing to address your emotions and what they're trying to say to you, you will never realize what you're truly capable of. Part of your work is to deal with your personal emotions, because the more you can deal with them, the more peace you will find. Why are people so afraid to deal with issues? It's much easier to gossip, judge others, or feel angry than to face our own insecurities. However, it is so much more empowering to sit down and talk with another and let your heart speak openly and honestly when you run into an issue or problem.

Tornados bring massive devastation, and yet they only last a few minutes. They pass through, leaving behind enormous havoc and destruction in people's lives. But in most cases, the devastation brings people together to support each other and rebuild their neighborhood. While people lose most of their material possessions in a storm of this magnitude, there is always a way to bounce back through uniting and working together. Emotional tornados are the same—we sometimes put ourselves in situations where we feel the full impact of an emotional storm, but how we choose to respond matters most.

A storm brings change. It is there to encourage the development of the muscles of our mind and heart so we can negotiate and navigate through adversity.

People love the thrill of the roller coaster. Nothing gets the blood pumping faster than surrendering to the danger and totally letting go. It may only be for a few seconds when you hit a big drop, your emotions explode, and you let loose yelling at the top of your lungs to really express how you feel. On the other hand, you might hate every second of it, but the exhilaration you feel when you reach the end of the ride fills you up with the excitement of knowing you faced your fears and survived! Emotions are your best friend when you honor and acknowledge them, and this helps the storm pass through even quicker.

Emotions are like a satellite dish—they catch every signal out there. You have to learn to build your own geo-fence, a virtual reality barrier. It's part of the process. When a plane takes off into a strong headwind, it needs all its force to lift itself off the tarmac into the air and find its flight path. Likewise, your own head needs all possible healthy energy and an imaginative and creative mindset that will shift your perspective and get you up and running. When you can imagine something, tie your heart to what you want to create, and then follow through, does it become possible? Once you understand the individual functions of mind and heart and unite them as a whole, then it is easier to do. It really is only doable when your heart and mind work together.

You have choices to make every second of the day. You can spend your life focusing on what you missed out on or regretting choices you made, or you can give yourself a break from all that unnecessary stress. You can never go back to the place where you made a certain decision, either to do something or not to do it. That moment has passed. The decision was made and is irreversible. What's done is done. You can cause more damage by digging a deeper hole trying to reverse what was done. You really do not have any control over the past, but you can determine how you navigate forward from here in the present. Do yourself a favor and don't live in regret.

Of course, there is no assurance that you will be in a different place, but your navigational system will become more experienced through the trial and error of taking detours and shortcuts. Just know that in due course, universal law will get you where you are meant to be. It's the universal law.

EXPEDITION 28

WHAT ARE YOU CREATING?

♥

The intention of my work is to inspire you to see yourself as a powerful creator in this world. My part consists of providing some guidance, reflections, and help along the way that's based on my life experience and passion to live in conscious awareness of what is possible. I'm happy to share the lessons I learn. I see myself as a connector, or facilitator, who brings people together. I am continuing to write and hope to find others to connect with through deep conversations about creating a healthy world for the majority of humanity.

My dream is to keep creating and doing my work in the world. It's all about creation now, whether it's a conversation, writing, healthy living, or playing. Every day is an opportunity to learn in the school of life, which has no graduation date. A young man recently reached out to me after his father told him I was a published author. Austin said he wanted to write short stories and wondered if we could talk. Between my launching of this trilogy and his busy baseball schedule at school, we managed to find time to have a call. I wondered how I could help him, because I write nonfiction. But between the time he reached out to me and the day of our call, he'd decided his passion was to write for young adults facing depression and anxiety. He shared how he'd been abused by his father and didn't want other young people to feel alone. He told me about how his stepdad and other figures in his life had helped him heal. And now, he wants to offer guidance to young people. I shared that I write because I wished these books had been available when I needed them. And I discovered that is why he wants to write. I am so looking forward to supporting him on his journey, wherever it takes him.

One call or connection can be a source of creation. The world does not need to be saved or made better for us to be "successful." There are opportunities around us every second of every day to create something meaningful. Isn't it time, more than ever, for those of us who are ready to live fully? I hope you are connected to your own bold and beautiful voice and understand that change comes from within. A new world cannot emerge unless you have clarity about why you are here and are finding ways to thrive as a powerful creator. Create playgrounds, not battlegrounds, in your environment—when you're ready. The artist within you has a very powerful role to play in humanity's evolution. Your heart and soul have a deep need to articulate love and compassion through whatever path you choose to experiment with. Experiment until you feel at home in your body and the world, on your own terms as the author and producer of your life.

Everyone wants love. Some people know it, and others are still waking up to our deep connection to nature and all that is possible when we choose to become health conscious. Love is vast and all-encompassing and goes far beyond the image of the traditional romantic relationship. Until we open up to this all-inclusive love and its diversity, we will not be able to experience the full range of what is possible.

The more you practice and embrace love individually and collectively, the more peace and harmony will descend on our world through your actions. If someone has not been able to experience kindness and compassion, it's more difficult for them to know what love is and be able to share it with others. Do an online search for "love," and you will get millions of hits from all over the world and from all walks of life. People are desperately seeking to understand love and to experience it. Maybe your purpose and mission is simply to know love for yourself, and knowing this will shift your mindset to create more love in the world in simple ways.

Everyone knows about romantic love that makes your heart flutter and makes you doubt yourself when you first meet someone. However, this is only one aspect of love. Letting your heart open up to a glorious sunset or an awe-inspiring vista of forest and mountain ranges can also expand your heart as it takes in the majestic beauty of nature. There is also the love of doing something that makes your heart sing, whether it's playing with your kids, reading a book, hanging out with people you enjoy, or spending time alone.

Then there is pure, unconditional love for self that will sustain you through everything. You can develop it more fully through interactions with others and challenging situations that ask you to question your value. Self-love releases you from the invisible jail cell and teaches you how to experience deeper love. It can rip you apart, only to open you up again to prepare you for the next chapter of your journey.

We have lost pieces of ourselves in the modern world. They have been replaced with walls of separation so high that it takes a lot of effort for us to trust ourselves and each other to come together around a shared purpose to make things happen. It's a wonderful feeling when you do experience a group of people coming together to cocreate. The incredible energy transmitted by everyone fires you up even more.

Many of us are hungry for this healthy energy. When you obtain it, you know you are enough, your values are clear, and you want to share yourself with the world. It starts with self-love. By loving and being kind and gentle with yourself, you can then play with others and spread your inner light with pure joy. I hope you give yourself permission to experiment and play as much as you can handle.

THERE IS A PATH WAITING FOR YOU. ONLY YOU CAN TAKE IT.

It is said that if you can see your path laid out in front of you, it's not your path. Your own path is one you make with every step you take. That's why it's *your* path. This path only makes itself visible when you are ready. It requires you to take your blinders off and deal with deep-seated issues within. This path has twists and turns and peaks and valleys to scale. It's not as simple as choosing between this or that and staying mired in belief systems that are not your own.

In Lund, I met Jai, a vibrant young woman who shared stories of her life, which I found fascinating. Both she and her then-partner lost their jobs when the organization they worked for asked them to tell the truth about what was happening behind the scenes. They both ended up losing the jobs they loved, forever. They learned early on that it did not serve them to trust a company to accept the truth despite being asked to share it. They went through a very turbulent time and eventually decided to part ways. Can you imagine losing the job you wanted to have for your entire life because, when asked, you told the truth and were promised safety if you did?

Jai's entire relationship with work shifted as a result. She could no longer define herself by how she made a living or give her trust to organizations that didn't care about her well-being. But it was not an easy path, as their dream jobs no longer existed and living in a small community meant fewer choices. A lot of healing needed to take place, but it was challenging because they had just bought their first home and had two young lives depending on them. The PTSD and the trauma they'd endured contributed to ending their marriage. Although many doors closed and they struggled, some new pathways slowly opened.

This remarkable young woman was brought up by a generation who taught her to "suck it up" and suppress her truth. That's how her society guided her and it was all she knew. Luckily, her mother, Pat, is an entrepreneurial farmer, and as Jai witnessed her mother's business expand, she realized she had a strong woman in her life who took many risks and explored different paths. Her mom's obsession with growing healthy food, working the land, and running an honor system in the store gave her a deep-rooted connection to what was truly important in life.

While the initial job loss that resulted in her divorce caused her deep stress and depression, Jai now understands that it helped her live her life in her own way. She shares her story and life openly. She feels a strong responsibility to make sure her children have a different relationship with the world than she had. And to do so, she is doing her best to help them be *their* best. When they feel sad, she talks to them about it and listens. Her two sons are very different: One often speaks his mind, and she allows him to be who he is. Her eldest, who is eleven, has an uncanny ability to tell her the truth, and she asks for his advice often. Jai is a powerful creator, and she never stops experimenting with what's possible. She even reinvented homeschooling during the pandemic, with the help of her boys. It's so exciting to know that women like Jai are stepping into their power and creating what we need most, no longer waiting to be picked.

Being able to see where you are and becoming aware of how you got there is key. As you also become conscious of the potholes in our current systems, instead of complaining about them, you can take physical action to create a healthier path for yourself and future generations. And you have to be aware of what beliefs are holding you back and assess your potential to shift.

Our "look at me" culture is part of the false reality that is impacting our health. When you fight in the current system, dispensing Band-Aids on old wounds, you remain stuck. You have to be ready to move beyond and create your own potential. You need the vision to break through the delusions of being the best, making the list, and being awarded recognition by an outside force.

This is the old, decaying system of celebrity and nonsense. Who is more fulfilled, the person who was on television for five minutes and needs the next hit to feel important or the person who impacts the lives of others as a parent, friend, or community member but no one knows their name? Why do we even have lists of the most generous people and give them awards? Does that not defeat the purpose?

Some days we get so stuck in the hamster wheel (which can easily happen) that we forget we have choices. There are so many opportunities available now, and the key question to ask is, do I allow fear to hold me back, or do I trek into the unknown with curiosity?

There is no magic button in real life. It takes conscious awareness that involves dedication and persistence in learning. No one is here to save you from yourself—that is *your* unpaid job. At the same time, you can become aware of people who can support you in healthy ways.

There are many amazing developments and opportunities in our chaotic world that you can only see when you start controlling the volume dial on the never-ending noise streaming into your life. We are seeing the start of conscious businesses, healthier news sources, ways to have more open dialogue, alternative education, and leaders focused more on people than profit.

The more you fight the current system, the more you lose. When you get real with the opportunities in front of you and create, you will evolve into a healthier existence. It is already happening on the edges.

What if, instead of being the first or the best in a crowded market where everyone craves the spotlight, you dedicated your life to becoming a healthy version of yourself?

If you're dependent on other people's opinions of you, then be prepared to be offended for the rest of your life. You can stay stuck in the old system and complain about the injustices, or you can step out and create. There are billions of people hanging on to dear life right now, resisting change and simply moving the deck chairs on a sinking ship, expecting different outcomes.

The current systems are rotting right in front of our eyes, and they can only be replaced when people wake up to their power in a healthy way, not wanting to dominate or win at all costs. We have seen how these movies end, every single time.

It scares many people to step out and grab the choice they truly want to make. But what if you face your fears? What is truly restricting you? And why are you holding on? Challenge what is restricting you by asking yourself, what's the opportunity here? What choice can I make? Instead of outlining a goal, try exploring without a plan. The field of possibility is where we get to play in this century. It is available to everyone, equally, when we live in awareness and not in fear. The more you choose to interact with the opportunities, the more you will find others who want to play and create with you.

Is this journey easy? It depends. For some, it is easier to follow the existing recipes and manuals of life. And if that makes you happy, then more power to you. You are in charge of your own operating system. When you meet a strong person, who is grounded in who they are and is not playing the fake game our society dictates, you will feel their energy coming from within them. Whether they are rich or poor, do not doubt that there is a deeper story inside. If you ask them what darkness they faced and conquered, they will likely share a deep story that is hidden from most people. Mountains do not emerge without earthquakes.

At the center of creation is flow and harmony. When you open yourself to all of life—the darkness and the light—you can face the big waves that crash on you when you are in their way. The next set of waves will continue to come, and how you anticipate and react to them is in your hands. But when you choose to face your darkness as well, you will push yourself outside of your comfort zone and look at the beliefs that may be keeping you from living in healthier levels of awareness. You will initially walk the tightrope of the broken system, but do not lose hope that the healthier one is waiting for you to emerge. It will be uncomfortable at first, but who said that we must have comfortable, safe lives?

When you can see your true potential and recognize that everything is here to be discovered, you will see a path full of opportunities. Hate and fear will no longer be the status quo at either the individual or the collective level of reality.

IT'S UP TO YOU

Everything in life can be a fantastic adventure—or not. It's a conscious choice about what energy you tap into. When you are headed into the future, which is unknown, it's all still a mystery. The unknown by itself has so many elements to experience, from fear to anticipation to hope to joy. You can always imagine and dream. But you can never really know what will happen when you take yourself out of the conventional manual to pursue your own path.

No one has walked in your shoes until this very moment. Every step is a mystery to uncover. You can be surprised or you can be disappointed or heartbroken. You can go in so many different directions. But the beauty of looking back at your life is that it shifts your view when you look forward.

Wisdom comes with experience, when you pay attention to life. It is up to you to step out of your story, and often your own drama, to truly see. Nothing is ever as it seems, and you can strip away the layers of belief to find the essence for you. Life can feel like a huge roller-coaster ride, with highs and lows and twists and turns that come to teach you. When you are ready to customize your ride and understand your inner power, much will shift, because you will be stepping out of someone else's story to create your own.

If the mind is like a cinematic projector and your life is the movie playing out on the screen, feeling frustrated by what you see is pointless. Try changing the reel running in the projector. Weed out limiting beliefs and societal conditioning that are holding you back. Vow to make your mind and heart work for you rather than against you! The most constricting barriers you build are not made from material things like steel but are infections of the mind, with stories that jail you in an invisible prison of belief. Unlike most jails, being stuck in life does not entail guards or physical bars to keep you imprisoned. The only person who can release you, or give you parole, is you. You don't have to ask anyone for permission. It's a time to be curious, get in touch with your imagination, and find courage and boldness for action. It's about finding your path, a deep purpose that propels you. Find a way out of the insane rat race that humanity has constructed that tells you how to live your life.

You may think for a moment that the sky is falling, and yours may definitely have fallen, but the more experiences you accumulate, the more you become aware that difficult experiences come to challenge and teach you so you can shine a light on another path.

It is not always an easy journey, but when you choose to see life as an adventure, it is about taking the roads less traveled and imagining what is possible. When you understand how powerful your mindset can be in how you respond, you will no longer be a victim of circumstance. You will no longer need to blame anyone as you turn in to yourself to heal and grow. When you become self-aware, your imagination is sharper and your ability to navigate helps you sense both the dangers and the opportunities that are right there for you to discover. It is no one's job to convince anyone of how life should be. But hitting the top in life or hitting bottom can happen to any of us. What you do when you get there is where the beauty lies.

The past is in the past and that's where you should keep it. You don't have to live there. You can only change yourself when you are looking to tear down the veils of memory that haunt you. You are here to learn, and the past serves as a teacher but not as a place to dwell or get yourself stuck in. When you don't learn from your past, you will repeat your stories until you do—whether it's a work situation or a relationship challenge. You should not deny your past experiences but see them as wondrous gifts. It's up to each of us to deal with past traumas or wounds so we can put them to rest. This is a time for connecting with your inner self, cutting toxic beliefs, and not brooding too much on what others have called your failures, for those aspects of your life probably weren't healthy for you. Allow things to fall away. Trust that you're making space in your life.

Your vision can get clearer and brighter when you are present and can see what you can go out and create. Without learning from a past experience, you might never be able to see a new idea or relationship emerging. Life allows you to develop these skills when you are ready to reveal what has been hidden and is waiting to be discovered.

While it is important to enjoy your own company and learn to savor time alone, there is also magic in connecting with people, especially with a shared purpose. It brings a certain lightness and enthusiasm to how you approach life. There is a special energy that emerges when you are united with someone who has a lightness of being. We all come from the same source, and our journey includes being aware of the loving energy emanating from within us. We have been programmed to seek love and acceptance outside of ourselves. But trying to please everyone and fit in to everything around us will drain our energy. The healthy alternative to the current societal conditioning is to question whether you are willing to operate your life on self-generated energy or whether you need to plug in to others to function.

The world needs you to reclaim your unique voice and power. Imagine your life with less blame, less judgment, less stress, less loneliness, less drama, and less of whatever else is keeping you distracted. How would it look? It is vital that we respect and appreciate our planet and realize we don't need as much as we think. We are much more than we realize. Pay attention to what is really happening, and show up and play your part.

Love is a good reason to be here. Know yourself intimately and discover your love for yourself so you can lift yourself and others up. It's time to do for yourself what you are willing to do for others.

If you can be truthful with yourself, then you can be truthful with anybody. Go beyond blame, beyond judgment, beyond should, could, and would. You must be willing to want to experience everything. When you want to experience everything, you will experience everything.

Remember, you are never truly alone. Physicist Stephen Hawking reminds us that we are here to connect and keep the conversation going: "For millions of years, mankind lived just like the animals. Then something happened which unleashed the power of our imagination. We learned to talk and we learned to listen. Speech has allowed the communication of ideas, enabling human beings to work together to build the impossible. Mankind's greatest achievements have come about by talking, and its greatest failures by not talking. It doesn't have to be like this. Our greatest hopes could become reality in the future. With the technology at our disposal, the possibilities are unbounded. All we need to do is make sure we keep talking."

Your life lessons never stop coming, but how you respond is key. Putting into action your gifts and abilities, your sense of creating, does not require that you receive anything in return. It is simply a flow of energy. But when it is aligned with truth and integrity, it will start a cascade of energetic orchestration and provide you with what you need.

When you know in your heart that there is nowhere to get to and that every moment of your life is your journey, you can look back at the impact you are having. Magic happens when your desire is not a rung on the ladder of success and you realize there is no real destination. No amount of proving yourself is required, but simply following your heart, becoming aware of your darkness, and tapping into your light. Your worth can never be taken away from you, because it is who you are when you show up fully in life for yourself and others.

GRAB HOLD AND MAKE IT YOURS

You can get sucked into the drama of the world or you can become more aware of the healthy undercurrents taking place around you and what role you can play. Today there is greater acceptance of alternative healing around the world. You may be seeking to understand the causes of an illness and how to fortify your immune system—not just on the physical level, but in the sense of how emotions and thought patterns affect your overall health. You may start examining the foods and products you are consuming and whether they inflame your body, for example. You may also become more aware of the lotions and herbs you are ingesting.

You increasingly understand that when you think of anything in the past that brings up fear or a tightness in your body, there is something there that it would be helpful to release. There's no longer a need to repress what you're feeling. If you're afraid for your future, become aware of the story you're telling yourself. What are you predicting for the future, and why? Maybe instead of seeing dire problems, start looking at opportunities that you might have access to or that you could create or participate in that would alleviate your fears. We are at a crossroads where the systems and programs and structures of our world are changing, and they are going to continue to change. Letting go of the virus of the mind—irrational fears—is the opportunity.

Go anywhere and you will find people complaining about the role of television and social media in our daily lives. But what happens when you realize that most of the media we have today is here as a tool for commerce, that the ultimate goal of brands and influencers is to hook you into whatever is being sold? It is we who are consuming the latest unsolved mysteries and doom-and-gloom programming of dystopian societies. And we're being fed more and more of the same through games and virtual reality. It's only when you become aware of what agendas you're consuming and stop buying into them that anything will change. I'd love to see creators in these businesses develop heart-centered programming that doesn't put us in a state of fear. People all over the planet have become connected through the invisible yet tangible energy paths of the internet. Isn't it time to have open conversations and explore how a healthy system can be implemented, whether in education, media, health care, government, business, or the legal or financial fields?

This is a time to *not* take sides, a time to move away from societal conditioning of right and wrong. The first step is to actually see the deep divisions and how they impact your life. Ask what aligns to your heart's truth. You do not have to convince others of your truth—let them find their own. You can slowly stop taking sides in a world that, by design, wants to keep you divided in conflict. As we explored in *F*ck the Bucket List for the Adventurer*, does it serve you to fight for your life? It doesn't mean that you ignore the past, but there's a healthier way to bring us together. It's done by creating healthy lives rather than raging against the machine and fighting authority figures who want to control us.

Looking for justice and fairness in corrupt systems is simply no longer viable for many of us who want to lead fulfilling lives. You have a choice in every situation: whether to be compassionate or judgmental. When peace and unity replace hatred and separation, a great transformation occurs. The flow of life is calling you. Imagine being on a raft in a river and seeing rocks and a waterfall ahead. When you live in fear, you will most likely drift toward the rocks. But when you take action and direct your raft, you will anticipate and navigate away from obstructions.

The healthy change you experience in the world will happen when you step into your power and become part of a bigger chain that connects you to a community in a meaningful way, working toward a shared goal. Isn't it time our education system stopped focusing on socializing young people to add to the gross national bottom line (creating workers) and started focusing on how to foster greater creativity?

We hold the power to shape the subjects and methods being taught to children by listening to young people. They are our future, and how we raise them matters deeply, as they don't accept the status quo. Young people today are more connected to nature and the Earth than other generations, and they will teach us about the importance of taking care of our environment and establishing new beginnings in human potential. It's time to question everything, especially who has authority over your life and whether it's healthy for your well-being.

When you are birthing something new into the world, many people will try to deter you because it has never been done before. But whose voice will you listen to? Do you dare to be who you really are and to let go of who you believe you're supposed to be? Isn't it time to throw back the curtains on your window of the world and let your light out? At the same time, let the light in. Expand your sense of what is possible. The truth never lies. Only you can release yourself and do the hard work of being truthful with yourself.

And then, find the others who want to walk the path with you.

EXPEDITION 29

TRUSTING YOUR HEART

♥

Each one of us is here to do our own work—no one can do it for us. Allow whatever no longer serves your well-being to drop away from you. Set your own natural pace and rhythm; there is no need to rush. You really don't want to carry around those heavy suitcases everywhere you go on your life journey. Clearing them out will help you stop dragging them around. When you no longer mask the deep whispers of your heart, you will question everything and listen to what's calling you. This will clear your path so you can step into healthy choices, healthy challenges, and healthy opportunities. It requires you to learn a completely new way, one of freedom from limiting beliefs and bucket list items that were never yours to begin with. It takes commitment and hard work to push yourself beyond your limits, especially when your gut tells you that you are on your path and you learn to always pay close attention to what is calling you. One of the greatest scientists of our time, Albert

Einstein, invites us to become aware that "the only real valuable thing is intuition."

Trusting your intuition can sometimes lead to difficult choices, such as letting go of people who don't support you, even people you've spent a lot of time with. The truth is that there is always a way. You may not always like the door that opens up to you or the choices you make, but there is always a way forward. You might find yourself a bit disappointed when you realize that the guy you walked away from is now a multimillionaire or that the project you worked on with the narcissistic people became an overnight success and you didn't benefit from the success yourself. But you have no regrets because none of it was calling you. You saw that underneath the money and success there was vast emptiness, and you chose to walk away from toxic people and situations. The cost of staying was too high for your health. Cutting ties with people who hurt you or are simply toxic to your well-being is an important step to consider. And if you release them, you can also release the part of you that invited them into your life.

YOU ARE ENOUGH

If you've ever experienced it, you know that this is one of the best feelings in the world: being able to practice what ignites you and share it with others. When you have a healthy relationship with money and are aware of what you actually need to live a fulfilling life, you're able to make more of what it is that brings money to you in the first place—your art, your craft, or your work. Your heart is a channel that helps you deeply understand what you want to create during your life. Feeling that you are not enough or that you don't have enough puts you in a scarcity mindset that brings daily struggles and challenges into your world. It takes work to shift your mindset from seeing problems everywhere you go to uncovering the opportunities within each challenging situation or person. It takes energy and persistence.

It's like planting an apple seed in the earth, sitting next to it, and expecting the apple tree to grow instantly so you can reach for a delicious, crisp apple immediately and eat it. It never works. It's a waste of energy. How many doubts will go through your mind if you just sit there and don't see any apples or anything happening because it's not the season when apples bear fruit? Imagine yourself standing in a field, planting seeds as you go through life. Which seeds do you want to plant? What impact will they have? What experiences will they create for you and others? All you need to do is imagine your seeds and then start the planting, knowing that not much grows wild overnight. Just plant and make sure that every seed contains healthy DNA. That's all you need. It's so simple that most of us struggle with this mindset.

Katherine Montero had a dream of becoming a scientist specializing in genomics as she entered the gates of Harvard Medical School. As a teen, she arrived in the Bronx from the Dominican Republican and her family dealt with many of the challenges new immigrants chasing the "American dream" faced—from serious financial difficulties to struggling with and adapting to the new culture and language. She experienced firsthand the deep divisions in her new society and no longer took for granted the simplicity of life back home where her grandmother showed her what it was like to be a businesswoman—making ends meet and always believing in yourself.

While working at Harvard Medical School, Katherine found herself hearing more and more stories about disadvantaged high school kids struggling to make their way in the world. During her lunch breaks, she started to architect ways to break these cycles by supporting local and international low-income youth. She knew in her heart that when the youth knew that someone cared about them, they would be able to change the course of their lives. To learn firsthand about the barriers and opportunities young people faced, she left her dream behind to work directly with young people as a teacher in schools across Massachusetts and started a social enterprise.

Katherine is now the Chief Executive Officer of Global Deeds, a social enterprise that works with teachers, public schools, and corporations in empowering disadvantaged youth through innovative education and employment. "It helps the students and youth until they achieve financial stability in their lives," Katherine shares. "We create customized support systems that enable students to reach their potential as technically savvy, financially stable, and socially conscious citizens. The number of property deeds under the name of our alumni will be a very tangible indicator of our success as a program."

Katherine knows that by inspiring students to become the change themselves and step into their own power, they no longer need to wait for anyone to help or "save" them. It is no simple task and there always is a need to raise more funds to be able to lift more young people and give them an equal opportunity to live healthy and full lives. Katherine has an open invitation for any one of us to take part in these programs and is constantly building partnerships to create even more opportunities. For me, hers is a far more inspiring story than the financial success of a few celebrated individuals because I imagine when young leaders like Katherine make it "big," they will be reinvesting their profits in areas that benefit our society and planet while wanting to remain off the radar of celebrated success.

Katherine encourages today's youth, especially women, to take control of the choices they make. According to her, "Whenever you chase or value someone else more than yourself, you assume the subordinate position and put yourself at a serious disadvantage. Please love and respect yourself enough," she advises herself and others.

Every day is like a gift wrapped in a different color that you get to unwrap and experience. When you wake up in the morning and take a full breath of air, you are fueled to experience a brand-new day filled with mysteries to explore. Your calendar may tell you where you need to be at every minute of the day, but life will throw curveballs and give unexpected surprises; you never really know what each day will bring no matter how organized or prepared you may think you are. No matter how old you are, there is still much to learn and explore in every minute of every day. And we must recognize that some questions will never be fully answered—they remain a mystery. Often, wisdom comes from the question and the journey you take to explore the sacred mystery called life.

The universe is inviting you to let go and flow with the waves of change. Realize that change is happening whether you like it or not and that you can resist it or not. You decide whether the future will be challenging and hard or exciting and rewarding. Much changes when you understand that you don't need to live in a drama, with roles like victims and villains who fight and find fault. You do not have to play the role of the victim. Life gives you everything you need—both positive and negative—to rise and shine and learn so you can create healthy ways of living instead of applying Band-Aids to open wounds.

It is up to you to find your own power and appreciate the beauty in adversity. When you understand what you are here to learn, you will discover what your soul longs for instead of needing to constantly gratify your ego's unhealthy demands. By learning how to trust your intuition and develop a healthy ego, you can listen to what your soul is whispering to you. You can feel whole by integrating your body, mind, and heart in realizing who you are and why you are here, connecting to your intuition and reclaiming your power in a world that tries to make you like everyone else.

You can stay stuck in the darkness of judgment and victimization, or you can step into the light of every situation and live at a higher level of awareness, where you put down your sword and find others to create with rather than to fight with. You can't always learn how to take impeccable care of yourself in this world of rules. Give yourself the gifts of healthy food, rest, and time to be creative and process what is happening in your life. It is not always easy to speak your truth and find inner peace. To do so, you need to find out what beliefs are holding you back and need to be purged, which judgments you are willing to self-correct. Letting go can only take you to a healthier place when you let the adversities teach you, the synchronicities guide you, and the inspirations nourish your mind and soul.

When you stop and make time for yourself, you can go back in your mind and tap into your creativity and imagination. You can edit your thoughts and trust that the next chapter of your life will be way more exciting and fulfilling when you do your own work first. But when you hold on to the past, you are stagnantly living the same story over and over, which usually brings with it dis-ease to the physical and mental body. You do not need to settle for anything but to live a life that is genuine for you and your environment. When you can stop warring within yourself, you will find a place where you are more in balance because you will live in a higher state of awareness. And then you can connect with those who want to support you, not fix you.

TRUSTING THE CURRENTS

When you're grounded in reality and tapping into your imagination, your trust in your intuition will continue to grow. You can stop not only to listen but to get clear on the direction the path is taking you. Teach yourself when to begin, which is not always simple.

Narrated by Addie Mae Aubrey, *Trusting the Currents* is a spiritual story of self-discovery—of faith, courage, forgiveness, and the uneasy search for one's place in life. Author Lynnda Pollio and Addie Mae, two remarkable women from different times and places, embark on an uncommon journey. Addie Mae had several strong women who loved and guided her in learning life's lessons. Her beloved high school teacher told her, "Words are cathedrals for ideas, Addie Mae. Each time we open a book, we enter a door to a sacred space where fresh truths are born. Reading changes what we are into who we might be, opening shuttered minds and warming even the coldest hearts. It frees our true promise like butterflies experiencing life for the first time outside the dark unknowin' of their cocoon."

Remind yourself as often as you need to that this is your life. Not anyone else's. People around you do their best to provide you with guidance and tools. But there are no absolutes. Coming into your own melodic harmony, balance, and peace means trusting the truth in your heart. No one has your answers, even when they mock you or cheer you on. You can spend time on your own in natural surroundings as a way to let yourself breathe and find peace. But please, ask your own questions, because no one else owns them more than you.

Some days I wake up with a plan or a list (it is very rare, but it happens), and when I do, I am almost always disappointed. Sure, my lists have gotten shorter, but my definition of achievement has changed dramatically. I have learned to trust the currents in life. When I wake up at two or three in the morning and feel a need to write, I write. Life moved me to a remote location so I could write these books. I thought I was coming here to build an academy with people who shared my vision, but that was a colossal failure. And now I know it was never meant to be. It was my lesson to learn that when I said yes to others, I should not do it at my own expense. I left San Francisco for this dream and some days I miss my life there, but I don't want that life back. My life has not been easy. I have learned to pay attention as the lessons keep arriving and the mastery comes from practice and breaking patterns. There are close to eight billion people on our planet, so I get to walk away from unhealthy people and situations by finding my own courage, taking risks, and seeing life as a gigantic experience. One of my favorite authors, Paulo Coelho, reminds me that "when I had nothing to lose, I had everything. When I stopped being who I am, I found myself."

Everyone can find their own way, and you never know where one choice, one decision, one connection can lead. I have no idea exactly what is next for me and I am not waiting for a sign, since I know in my heart that it will be revealed and I will meet the other crazy people who want to step out and build bridges to a healthy world here on Earth. All I bring with me is the expansive belief that anything and everything, like nature, can change in a heartbeat. Addie Mae's whispers remind me that knowing "when to swim with strength and courage, and when to surrender to the changing currents is all [you] need to find [your] true way."

When you are ready to live a full life as an explorer, you can put down your list and be honest with yourself. Listen to your heart and align it to your healthy mind, so you can discover your own unique answers. You are capable, at any point in your life, of creating. What is it that you want to create? What opportunities do you see? What risks scare you? Will you trust the unexpected to happen?

EXPERIENCING LOVE INCLUDES
THE HEARTBREAKS

We are shifting in a world where experiencing life will become more important. While many people fear change, it's time to recognize that change is simply a part of life; it is the natural flow of life. Nothing in nature lives for itself. Nature teaches you to connect and adapt. Trees don't consume their own fruit and rivers don't drink their own water. When you can become more aware of the universal law of nature that surrounds you in every moment of every day, you may see the world with greater intuition and imagination. While some people prefer security over risk-taking, this is a time of opportunity to bring different thinking into the world.

Many people today are so busy climbing the ladder of success that they don't remember why they wanted to be successful. But everyone wants to get "there," and once they do, they may have a moment of glory but soon find out that it, too, is fleeting. Fame and power feed the ego, and the ego can never be satisfied when all you are pursuing is acclaim and validation from others.

Life is about your ability to imagine, dream, and create. It is so essential that you dream. When you give up dreaming, you give up on your life. Dreaming and living go hand in hand because that is where you tap into your relationship with your life and accept who you are and why you are here.

You can only receive the amount of light that you can absorb. We each have our hand on our own dimmer switch and can turn it up or down. Do you feel you are in charge of your own switch, or is someone else controlling yours? What I have learned through trial and error is that in instances when it seems to get too dark, I have the ability to let more light shine in. The sun shines during the day and disappears at night. Likewise, there are patterns and cycles in our lives where we experience dark moments. Can you accept them so you can begin to move through them and out the other side? Remember, *it is always darkest just before dawn.*

When you can connect with your inner self, you can find harmony within yourself. There are tests and challenges along the way allowing you to adjust, transform, and unlearn so you can relearn, reimagine, reinvent, and rebuild yourself. Every one of us has been wired with an enthusiasm to explore and question and a huge capacity for compassion.

Human history repeats itself and will continue to do so if we do not break the cycle. And your life will bring you the same lessons and people over and over until you start doing your work. Our systems are cracking, and it's time to see the opportunities that are emerging instead of looking only at the problems. As you watch history repeat itself, you have two basic choices: you can recognize that you have already seen this movie and its sequel before and therefore you can predict how it will play out next time, or you can start creating a different story. It's a choice.

You can criticize, complain, and blame others for what is happening around you, or you can see what is possible and create. In a world that constantly tries to make you like everyone else, it's time to release what no longer serves you. It is an opportunity to make room for what *does* serve you and help you create a more meaningful path.

Many of us have been conditioned to take care of everyone else before ourselves. We are conditioned into a culture of sameness where we are told to keep up with the latest fads and trends. At school, we are measured according to everyone else. At work, there are internal lists that tell us whether others see us as high performers or not. There is a one-size-fits-all, cookie-cutter mentality, but in reality, cookie cutters only work when we're baking cookies. And you are not a cookie.

The opportunity is to ask yourself tough questions and go deep into your soul to find out what you are made of. Regardless of what anyone else may think is cool, hip, or trendy, what is it that you want your imprint to be? What sets you on fire? How can you share your ideas with generosity, speak up, and shine a light in the world? The opportunity in front of you is to shift the focus away from fear and negativity and speak the language of music collectively in harmony. Our collective future depends on how you choose to live your life.

We are not born into this world with twenty-twenty vision. It takes time to focus and see and discover what is already here. It's been said that if you could see everything that is actually here, you would die immediately, as it would overpower your senses. It takes time to dissolve into something healthier. Dissolution is a process where you maintain whatever feeling you've come with while at the same time begin to adapt to whatever new idea is calling you. Change does not happen overnight and nature does not rush. We can't simply click our heels and be physically transported to another location—yet!

The mystery of why you are here and where you go when you die continues. And everything has a reason. Nothing is here just for the sake of being here. As a child, I always saw this as a fact of life and questioned the reasons behind everything. The older I get, the more I see the reason as so obvious—it's in everything we see, do, and feel. It is your ability to evolve and discover healthier paths and practices in a way that won't shock your system.

WHAT'S NEXT FOR YOU?

Scientific research shows that poets and great scholars throughout history were wise to trust their intuition. There is fact-based research showing that the heart has intelligence and plays a particular role in our experience of emotions. Some things can sound impossible and still be true. One day you wake up and feel wisdom that was planted deep inside your soul that opens you to seeing possibilities for the first time. It all depends on when you are ready to listen to your calling. Just like old structures that no longer support an emerging world, old beliefs convince you they are protecting you from foolish ideas. They hang on for dear life, mocking you for believing there is another way, judging you for thinking that you can build new bridges that are healthy for yourself and others.

Life depends on your seeing beyond what you have been led to believe is true. And in our world, the status quo loves new trends that others endorse and celebrate first, because they are simply afraid to follow their own heartbeat. If they did, it might change who they believe they are, and uncertainty and the unknown are scary destinations for many people. It is easier to save someone else or even to save the world, because that doesn't require personal work. I have gotten in trouble many times for speaking my mind about what I see. I played the game for a while but found it too confining and limiting—there is no map or guide to where I am headed. Some said I was foolish, but after a while some started to see the bridge, and then accepted it as a fact as more people joined. Now, they judge anyone who thinks in the old ways.

What no one tells you is that who you are now and what you are now does not determine how you want to show up in the world now. As for me, I try different things to see what sparks my soul. I listen to what life is calling to me, even when the sound is a faint whisper. I have also ignored very loud signals at my own expense. I have taught myself to walk away from safety when it feels too confining. I am here to build and create with people who want to do it from the heart in healthy ways. I have crazy ideas that are way ahead of their time. I want to go places with others who are brave enough to create things for ourselves, and I know that is in the next chapter of my life.

An eye for an eye only makes the world blind. Poet Mary Oliver helps us see that "though I play at the edges of knowing, truly I know our part is not knowing, but looking, and touching, and loving, which is the way I walked on." No one knows who created the sun, the earth, the air, the animals, the plants, or the ocean. But we do know who created money, jobs, football, the internet, social norms, the theory of relativity, the health care system, wars, and sports. This world has been constructed with the expert, the leader, the authority figure, the guru standing in front of the crowd, and a commoditization of the wisdom of the crowd, which has yet to be truly unleashed.

Experts spend hours practicing what they'll say and reading from scripts the words that they hope will inspire you to buy into their messages. TED Talks, for example, are a beautiful concept and were supposed to be a pure exchange of ideas, but they have become a one-way consumer industry with not much dialogue or true exchange. The next time you find yourself being seen as part of the audience of a concert, film screening, or theatre performance, be wary of becoming an audience to someone else's scheme. If you are in a physical space, you can pick up your chair, create a circle with others, and have a meaningful dialogue about what matters. If you are online, there are many tools you can use to connect with others and have conversations that don't require a stage or someone giving you permission to speak. It's all in your hands and your heart when you pick yourself.

LISTENING TO YOUR HEARTBEAT

If you've experienced these books and understand their deeper meaning, you can tap into your highest potential by simply starting at your own pace. Nature doesn't rush—it simply exists. But if you are still angry with the world and want to follow the manual of success, then go be angry and follow what is most meaningful to you. It's always a choice.

And if you feel it's time to navigate yourself, I'm grateful you are here and I look forward to hearing your story. I'm following my own guidance, so if you feel called, please don't hesitate to reach out to me. I wrote these books because I wished they had been available to me when I started on this path. And then I remembered that as someone who has made some hard decisions and failed a lot, it was my responsibility to bring this universal wisdom to light. And now we are here together, and I know firsthand that anything is possible as I follow the guidance in these books and jump into my next expedition—leaving Lund and becoming a digital nomad.

I have chosen the road less traveled, and I hope you'll join yours with mine. I care about your experiences and hope to touch the lives of many people who are ready to be powerful and healthy creators on this planet. I have been sharing openly to encourage you to open your mind and heart to life. What I care most about is that you have a beautiful life and that we create meaningful systems that serve us. No one else will do it for us. How can anyone who has taken the road less traveled not be changed? I do have one request. If you know someone who will be sparked by what is here, please share the books with them and have a conversation with them after their experience. You can also ask your local library to order the books. There's always a way.

When you choose to be a pioneer or a visionary, take a little risk. Everything is abundantly here to be discovered. There is nothing new under the sun. Our emerging world needs you to fall in love with what's possible, be the best you can be, and shine your light with love and grace. This is not an ending, just the beginning of your next expedition when you start seeing the picture, the concept, the sensations, and you make it happen. And to do so, you calm your mind and open the doors to your intuition. Your inner sight enhances your physical sight as you expand in total consciousness of being.

Poet Rainer Maria Rilke exhorts us to "be patient toward all that is unsolved in your heart and try to love the questions themselves, like locked rooms and like books that are now written in a very foreign tongue. Do not now seek the answers, which cannot be given you because you would not be able to live them. And the point is, to live everything. Live the questions now. Perhaps you will then gradually, without noticing it, live along some distant day into the answer."

Poet Mary Oliver asks, once again, "Tell me, what is it you plan to do with your one wild and precious life?"

And renowned martial artist Bruce Lee wisely shares, "Adapt what is useful, reject what is useless, and add what is specifically your own."

I leave you with this question: Why are you here? What are you ready to imagine and create as a healthy architect of humanity? Remember, one may be lonely but one never needs to be alone. What and who is calling you? What is at the heart of your own beautiful story?

WHAT'S NEXT?

EPILOGUE

♥

I f you've come this far on your journey, you know that by now, you have an incredible source of knowledge inside of you. When you become aware that there is a natural abundance on our planet, you do the work to free yourself from the mental prison of fear. This is a time when, instead of carrying your hurt, your doubts, or your sadness, you can consciously decide to trek into the unknown as a healthy creator of your life. You are here to experience life at your individual pace. And as you listen to your own heartbeat, you may realize that awareness is no longer enough—it must come with action!

You are the only one who can choose whether to continue fighting for your life within the old systems or create what you need—be it in mental health, alternative therapies, food security, healing the land, connecting with nature or the next wave of education, fashion, governance, business, finance, travel, media, film, music, or things we have yet to dream up. As author and healer Lynnda Pollio shares with us, "Don't stand under a collapsing building, trying to catch the bricks as they fall to put them back in place. Step back, allow the building to give way, then use the bricks to build something more beautiful."

So, What's Actually Next?

When you stop accepting the status quo as a way of life, it gets lonely, and it's challenging to find others on the path. We often want to connect with fellow creators, but there's nowhere to find them and have meaningful conversations to explore what's possible.

HeartPickings.com

Now that all three books are out in the world, I'm creating something I need myself: a healthy place to hang out, exchange ideas, connect, support, and truly collaborate with people who understand that there is another way to live our lives. The vision is that we can join forces around what we care about at HeartPickings.com as an online community.

This community is emerging because of the many heart-filled people who are showing up with their own missions like Kay Newton, Geoffrey Beulque, Jo Rawcliffe, Tim McDonald, Carol Chapman, Christopher Drummond, Lynnda Pollio, Donna Cravotta, Tara Sheahan, Dr. Natalie Leigh Dyer and many others. You perhaps?

Can you embrace the unknown with gratitude and curiosity to create healthy systems that serve the majority of humanity? The first phase of HeartPickings.com will be an open portal where anyone can access trusted information, products and services about living well and discover resources supporting a healthy lifestyle—mind, body, and soul. HeartPickings is for you if you want to (re)learn what is healthy or toxic for you. Eventually, HeartPickings will be a by-invitation-only online community for those open-hearted and ready to trek into a brave new world.

If you made it this far in the journey, maybe you are here to be a powerful creator on our planet. Join us at http://heartpickings.com

IS THIS THE END OR THE BEGINNING FOR YOU?

JOIN A *F*CK THE BUCKET LIST* VIRTUAL BOOK CLUB

Hiitide.com offers authors and readers abundant virtual book clubs. Have you ever wanted to translate the wisdom in books into a shared daily practice? Now you can. Over 28-days, you can engage in daily journals, exercises, and group discussions delivered in short, easy-to-complete bites you can integrate into your life. And I will pop in for a session to listen and grow with you.

You also have an option to host a book club and build your own community by sharing your love of reading with friends and community members through an easy invitation process. And then use the message board feature to share insights, stay connected, and facilitate discussions. Hosts earn a percent of the revenue from their members that sign up and keep the revenue or donate it to a social cause.

Join us at Hiitide.com

DEEP GRATITUDE
ACKNOWLEDGMENTS

♥

This trilogy would not have been possible without the rich life I have been blessed with—all the twists, all the experiments, and all the heartbreaks and love I have experienced.

My father, Uri Baron, left the world when I was only twenty-six. He had a challenging life and gifted me with the knowledge that life is precious and is to be experienced fully. He taught me never to equate my self-worth with what I do for a living. I am forever grateful to my mother, Ruth Baron, who supported her crazy, rebellious daughter. And my sister, Anat Baron, a force of nature, making a huge impact in our world in her own way.

I am eternally grateful to all the people who openly share their stories on the pages of these books, offering guidance and wisdom from their own journeys and life experiences. And to my dear friend, Amy Aines, for deep conversations from our hearts.

There are so many people to mention who are in my heart and you know who you are.

And most of all, I am grateful to the universe for all the lessons, experiences, experiments, and unconditional love it continues to provide me as I become a digital nomad in May 2021 and trek into the unknown, trusting my heart as a healthy creator on the planet. I look forward to what is possible and hope to connect with you to create what is needed most in our world.

Printed in Great Britain
by Amazon

81280381R00127